'What kind

I am?'

'Dangerous!' ...
towards Christie sudd... ...k
with a gasp as she saw the extent of ... in
his dark eyes. 'I've never recovered from
trusting you, and I doubt if I ever will! You're
nothing but a lethal little black widow. I could
tangle spiders in the webs you weave, and
you're not weaving another one around me!'

Dear Reader

What a great selection of romances we have in store for
you this month—we think you'll love them! How about
a story of love and passion, set in the glamorous world of
the movies—with deception and double-dealing to thrill
you? Or perhaps you'd prefer a romance with the added
spice of revenge . . .? We can offer you all this and more!
And, with exotic locations such as Egypt, Costa Rica and
the South Pacific to choose from, your only problem will
be deciding which of our exciting books to read first!

The Editor

Sarah Holland was born in Kent and brought up in
London. She began writing at eighteen because she loved
the warmth and excitement of Mills & Boon. She has
travelled the world, living in Hong Kong, the South of
France and Holland. She attended a drama school, and
was a nightclub singer and a songwriter. She now lives on
the Isle of Man. Her hobbies are acting, singing, painting
and psychology. She loves buying clothes, noisy dinner
parties and being busy.

Recent titles by the same author:

DANGEROUS DESIRE

BLUE
FIRE

BY

SARAH HOLLAND

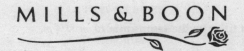

MILLS & BOON

MILLS & BOON LIMITED
ETON HOUSE, 18-24 PARADISE ROAD
RICHMOND, SURREY TW9 1SR

All the characters in this book have no existence outside the imagination of the Author, and have no relation whatsoever to anyone bearing the same name or names. They are not even distantly inspired by any individual known or unknown to the Author, and all the incidents are pure invention.

MILLS & BOON and the Rose Device are trademarks of the publisher.

First published in Great Britain 1994 by Mills & Boon Limited

© Sarah Holland 1994

Australian copyright 1994   Philippine copyright 1994 This edition 1994

ISBN 0 263 78694 3

Set in Times Roman 10 on 11¼ pt. 01-9410-56389 C

Made and printed in Great Britain

CHAPTER ONE

THE white Cadillac convertible sped along the coast of southern California. Christie sat in the front seat, blonde hair rippling in the hot breeze, a smile on her famous pink pouting mouth. This was turning out to be the best year of her professional life. She had just signed with Camarra Pictures for a further three movies, her last film had won her a nomination for best supporting actress at the Academy Awards, and now she had been given the crowning accolade of the Hollywood social scene—an invitation to a weekend party at Casa Camarra.

Her personal life was going wonderfully well, too. Glancing at the man beside her, she smiled, blue eyes tracing his austere profile with love. At forty, Simon was twelve years her senior, and today, with the California sea breeze in his blond hair and a debonair smile in his grey eyes, he looked very happy.

They were newly engaged, she and Simon Mordant, and the diamond solitaire on her finger flashed in the hot sunlight as a reminder of her long-standing relationship with him, and the lovely but surprising conclusion of marriage it was about to reach.

Suddenly, he turned to look at her and frowned faintly. 'What are you thinking about?' he drawled in his sophisticated New York accent.

'Oh . . . you.' She smiled.

He laughed. 'What about me!'

'Just that I can't believe it took us so long to realise we were meant for each other.'

'My dear, I knew it the minute I saw you. A vibrant beauty with talent, trapped in an awful British TV soap series. That girl, I said to myself, is destined for great things—I must get her by hook or by crook.' His grey eyes sparkled with amusement. 'And I did!'

'I like to think that your interest in me was more personal,' she pointed out, a frown marring her brow, because as far as she was concerned marriage was forever, and must be based on love, mutual respect, friendship—not strategic career moves.

'How could you doubt me, Christie?' He looked faintly hurt. 'We've been such very close friends for three years now. I've been with you at every step of the way, and what could be more natural than to eventually propose?' His smile was kind and loving. 'All right—we don't have a grand passion for each other. But I think we've both agreed that grand passions are dangerous.'

'Yes...' she said huskily, pain suddenly sheening her eyes.

'After all, Jared Buchanan taught you all about grand passions—and nearly destroyed you in the process.'

Jared seemed to rear between her and Simon like a ghost at a wedding feast.

The worst thing was that it was true—Jared had taught her what grand passion was. He had taught her how it consumed like the fires of hell, ever-burning, ever-present, and ever-destructive. It was a dark, dangerous way to love, but she couldn't forget it. What woman could? The fiery passion in his wild, dark eyes, the hoarse note in his voice when he was dizzy with desire, making love with a frenzied intensity that had driven them both to the brink of disaster.

Passion like that was dangerous, Christie thought for the millionth time, her blue eyes darkening with the memory. Mature love was what she needed—and what she had with Simon. A love based on friendship, mutual respect and twinned futures. Not a blazing intensity that wrought more havoc than a forest fire. Besides, Jared had said he loved her, but his behaviour had told a very different story.

Simon's behaviour, however, told her that his love was real, solid, stable, consistent and lasting. They had known each other for three years now, and for the first two years had been nothing but friends, business partners, living out here in Hollywood building their respective careers. It had been around seven months ago that Simon had first kissed her, and although the kiss didn't exactly set either of them on fire, it was the first kiss she had experienced for over two years, so she forced herself to lie back and enjoy it. Sweet, loving, tender Simon could not hope to ignite the fires Jared had tapped in her. But he kissed her often, and he loved her as a true friend—what more could she possibly ask for?

He was right. Marriage was the natural step for her and Simon now. They weren't lovers, and, to be honest, she knew that their wedding night would be as tame as their kisses. But at least she would be married to a kind, gentle man, and in no danger of the sort of hurt Jared inflicted.

'We're here,' Simon said suddenly, and as she looked up she saw the vast electronic gates of Casa Camarra, that fabled palace by the sea.

Palm trees towered against the tall white mansion, the turrets painted pale green, the smooth sleek lines almost European. It had been built by Eduardo Alfonso Camarra in the 1920s, when all of Hollywood glittered in silver-screened glamour. Now it was owned by Mike and Millie Camarra, his direct descendants, and the heirs to his film empire. They threw weekend parties, just as Eduardo Alfonso had, and although the glamour of the 1920s was long since gone, a weekend at Casa Camarra was still one of the most sought-after invitations in

Hollywood. Not only did one become part of the most élite set, but one also became part of Hollywood history, simply by having been a guest at a Casa Camarra weekend party.

'We've really made it now, haven't we?' Simon said beside her. 'A weekend at Casa Camarra! We're at the top of the heap!'

Christie smiled, delighted too by their joint success. She had always wanted to be a famous film actress, ever since she was a little girl, and often wanted to pinch herself to see if her dream-come-true really was just that—a dream. Last year, when she won her Oscar at the Academy Awards ceremony, she had found herself walking up those legendary steps in a glittering evening gown and thought, My God, how did I get here? How can this be real? And how many times have I dreamt of this moment, never truly believing it could ever happen? At home that night, thinking of her unhappy childhood, the mother who had victimised her, the sisters who had sneered at her, and the schoolkids who had laughed at her. Had any of them seen her on international television? Had all the people who had been so cruel to her watched her collect her award, applauded by the most talented people in the film world, her contemporaries and peers? She did hope that they had! After all—wasn't that what had spurred her on? Of course, her mother was long-since dead, but her sisters were alive and spitting poison every time Christie contacted any of them. The three witches, she had thought of them as when she was a child. They hated her even more now that she was famous than they had in childhood. She sent them Christmas and birthday cards—they never replied. But Christie believed in Karmic justice, and was convinced that one reason for her success was that she had never done anything malicious to anyone. Her reward was success, and as she sat in her luxurious Bel Air bedroom looking at Oscar, Oscar had looked serenely, impassively back at her, a symbol of absolute triumph, the pinnacle of all her dreams, and she had thought, Is this how it's done? So simply? Just my name read out from a card, then that walk up the steps to collect a little gold statuette? Ah, yes, it was always that simple, just so long as one did the hard work that led to that moment. And what a long, long road it had been, full of work, work, work and lost, lost love...

Now, she looked up at Casa Camarra and reflected, Jared Buchanan never loved me. If he had loved me, he would have understood why I needed to be famous. He would have been happy for me—not tried to stop me.

That emptiness came back into her heart. She pushed it away. I have Simon now, she told herself, and he does love me. Look how he's helped and supported me. Of course he's the right man for me.

The Cadillac came to a standstill. Birdsong filled the hot Californian afternoon, crickets chirping in the extensive grounds, and the sun blazed on the fabled white steps of the mansion.

'I thought I heard a car!' Millie Camarra came down the steps dripping with gold and glamour. 'We're all out by the pool, but I always come out to greet my guests properly—welcome to Casa Camarra!'

'It's wonderful to be here.' Christie got out of the car and embraced Millie, who was drenched in Giorgio perfume. 'Thank you so much for inviting us.'

'Oh, that English accent!' Millie laughed. 'I'm sure that's what makes the men go wild over you, Christie. It's at such odds with your come-to-bed looks.'

Christie gave a wry smile. 'Don't be embarrassing! I'm an engaged woman now, you know. Have you seen my ring?'

'In every Hollywood daily,' Millie drawled, but caught her hand for a closer look. 'My, my! You did go to town, didn't you, Simon? A diamond as big as the Ritz, as darling Scott Fitzgerald would have said.'

'Nothing but the best for Christie!' drawled Simon, white jacket slung over one elegant shoulder as he walked round the car, tall and blond and terribly Harvard. 'How are you, Millie? You look stunning.'

'Flatterer!' she laughed, patting her red hair. 'Come out back to the pool and say hi to everyone. Rodrigo will take your cases up.'

They followed her across the cavernous marble hallway, breathtakingly beautiful with its art deco chandeliers swinging forty feet above the white and black marble floor, a huge oil painting of Rudolph Valentino as the Sheikh on one wall, a painting of Jean Harlow in a long white silk gown on another, and further paintings of the Hollywood Greats lining the sweeping staircase that was just built for a leading lady to walk down.

Out through a long series of rooms they went, finally out through a pair of vast French windows, until suddenly they were in the sizzling heat of southern California, and the pool area was glittering in the sunlight.

'Look, everybody!' Millie clapped her hands, rings flashing. 'Christie McCall and Simon Mordant.'

'Hi!' nine or ten people called in greeting, all lounging around the vast pool, which was lined with white Roman statues. Christie recognised several faces—an actor with a legendary past as a womaniser, his latest actress girlfriend who was really only a bit-part player, a producer, his wife, and, of course, Mike Camarra, the head of Camarra Pictures.

'Mike!' Simon made a beeline for him at once, shaking his hand and taking the seat opposite him. 'Wonderful to see you . . .'

Millie moved up to Christie. 'Sit down, honey. What would you like to drink?'

'Cherry mineral water, please.' Christie instinctively walked to where Simon was and sat down, even though she found Mike Camarra something of a shark with his gold-toothed smile and his billion-dollar-deal eyes.

'. . . hear you made mincemeat of that little brunette actress?' Simon was saying.

'Sure did,' Mike Camarra drawled, scratching his tanned paunch. 'Sliced her up and fed her to the vultures. She'll never work in Hollywood again.' He winked at Christie. 'Don't worry, sweetheart—you'd never be stupid enough to try and take on Camarra Pictures in a lawsuit, would you?'

'I wouldn't dream of it,' Christie murmured wryly.

'One cherry, one peach.' A maid put the drinks on the table.

'So——' Millie sat down beside them '—only two more guests to arrive, now.'

'Anyone we know?' Christie asked politely.

'Well, sure.' Millie smiled right at her. 'Jared Buchanan and Nessa Vale.'

It was six seconds before anybody spoke. Christie was white and not breathing. Her hand clutched the iced glass so tightly she thought it might break. It can't be true, she thought in a state of shock. I must have misheard. She can't be telling me that Jared is coming here, at any moment, and that he'll be here for the whole weekend, hour after hour, minute after minute. . .

She wanted to speak, but her mouth was so dry she couldn't form the words, her tongue sticking to her palate. Like a stranded fish, she tried to lick her lips, and then she realised that Mike and Millie were amused by her emotional distress. There was only one explanation for that: they knew all about her and Jared's passionate love affair of the past, and they had set them up deliberately to see what would happen.

'Do you know Jared and Nessa?' Millie drawled with amusement.

Christie flicked an appalled gaze at Simon but, to her horror, found he was as white and speechless as she.

'My, my!' Millie laughed. 'Look at your faces! You'd think Attila the Hun and his girlfriend were coming!'

'His girlfriend?' Christie's raw voice echoed in the hot afternoon. 'Jared Buchanan and Nessa Vale are——?'

'Having a madly passionate affair? Yes, it's the talk of Hollywood!' Millie watched her with clever green eyes. 'Oh, but you've been away filming on location in Mexico, haven't you? You wouldn't know what the latest gossip was.'

'No...' Christie was so disturbed that she knew she couldn't stay out here, certainly not if Jared was going to arrive at any minute. But the shock was affecting her physically, and she found even the simplest movements difficult, her arm heavy and her hand shaking as she slowly, carefully set her drink down on the table and got clumsily to her feet. 'But I think I'd like to go to my room now. Freshen up. Settle in. Unpack. You don't mind, do you?'

'Not at all.' Millie got to her feet too. 'I'll have Rosita show you up.' She beckoned to a beautiful Spanish maid. 'How about you, Simon? Do you want to stay down here or——?'

The roar of a powerful car engine came distantly from the other side of the house.

'Ah!' Millie smiled and flicked those knowing green eyes back to Christie, murmuring, 'I expect that'll be Jared now.'

'Why don't you hang around and say hi, Christie?' Mike Camarra suggested, watching her as closely as his wife. 'Jared's a very powerful director. He could be good for your career.'

'If he's staying for the weekend,' Christie forced herself to look and sound calm, even though her heart was banging nineteen to the dozen, 'I'll have plenty of opportunity to get to know him.'

Millie laughed softly. 'Oh, yes, you'll have plenty of opportunity to "get to know him" this weekend! Your bedrooms are right next door to each other.'

Christie's breath caught. She stared at them both, white with shock. They definitely knew! Bedrooms next door to each other? Oh, God, this was a nightmare!

'Yes, madam?' The Spanish maid was at their side.

'Ah, Rosita!' Millie turned to her. 'Show Miss McCall to her room. I'll go and welcome Jared and Nessa.'

Christie began to move away with Rosita, her legs shaking beneath her, desperate to get to the sanctuary of her room, walking briskly, holding her breath, hoping her legs didn't give way before Jared walked into that stunning marble hallway.

Millie was walking rapidly to the open front doors. Car doors were slamming outside in the heat. Christie walked faster and faster, sweat breaking out on her upper lip.

'Jared! Wonderful to see you...'

Christie was halfway up the stairs, almost running now.

'Hello, Millie. Long time no see.' That dark, dangerous voice stopped her in her tracks just as she passed the vast painting of Vivien Leigh staring down in haughty beauty, dressed as Scarlett O'Hara in that infamous scarlet dress, the woman who had turned down her soulmate in Rhett Butler and lived to regret it.

Christie couldn't resist Jared Buchanan, soulmate and past lover, even though he had been perfectly able to resist her. She found herself turning, one damp hand clinging to the polished banister, staring over one slim, bare shoulder as her heart beat with violent passion and then twisted, sick with love, hate, desire and excitement.

Jared Buchanan stood in the vast doorway, magnificent, everything she had ever loved in a man, the sunlight framing his powerful body. He was dressed in black, with a tight waistcoat and crisp white shirt and black trousers, his expensive jacket slung casually over one broad shoulder. Hard muscles packed every inch of his six-foot-six frame with powerful masculinity and a sex appeal that made every woman who saw him want to give in to him—just as she had done. Did any man have the right to be so superb? Not only lethally sexy, but brilliant, clever, talented and ruthlessly hard-headed in business.

'You're the last to arrive,' Millie was saying.

'You said six o'clock, and it's only five.' His deep, cool voice was still holding Christie captive.

'Everyone else was early,' Millie laughed.

'Yes—who is everyone else, Millie? You were very cagey about the guest list when I——' He broke off suddenly, dark eyes catching the shimmer of gold hair and white dress on the stairs, flicking up abruptly to see Christie standing there watching him.

Silence.

The chandelier swung gently in the warm breeze.

Christie stood very still, so did Jared. Their eyes locked in a moment of shock. His face was wiped clean of expression as seconds ticked past and still he stared at her. Then his mouth tightened and rage leapt in those jet-black eyes.

'Christie McCall?' Jared looked down furiously at Millie. 'She's staying here for the weekend with us?'

'Why yes, Jared, darling! Did I forget to tell...?'

Christie turned and ran up the rest of the stairs before she could hear any more. Her whole body was leaping with fire, her heart pumping blood through her veins, making her at once exhilarated and afraid. Rosita was waiting on the landing for her and Christie almost collided with her, startled as she jumped back, apologising breathlessly, her voice shaking. Rosita gave her an intrigued little smile before leading her to her bedroom.

Once inside, Christie dismissed the maid and groped her way to the bed, sinking down on it, trembling from head to foot. Oh, God, how could this be happening? It was a nightmare. She couldn't begin to deal with it. Forty-eight hours, locked up in this house with Jared Buchanan—after not having seen him for three years, all those arguments left simmering inside both of them, the bitter recriminations, the anger and pain of rejection...how on earth was she going to cope with spending this much time with him? And his girlfriend, she thought savagely—Nessa Vale—one of the most respected actresses in Hollywood.

Jealousy seared her veins. She had known he would have other women after they split up. Jared had always had women throwing themselves at him, even when he was practically living with Christie in that lovely little flat just outside Elstree back home in England. Her heart ached as she remembered it all, and the feelings came flooding back to engulf her...

Suddenly, she noticed Ava Gardner smouldering down at her from an exquisite oil painting on the wall of her bedroom. Tough woman, Ava. Not for her sitting in tears on a bed thinking of the man she had loved when she should be trying to put herself into the Hollywood Hall of Fame.

Anger rushed through her. She was there to consolidate and further her career as a movie-star—not go into self-destruct over a gorgeous, dangerous, sexy man who had hurt her badly in the past and could easily do so again!

Think! she told herself, pressing her hands to her head. Think!

Why was Jared here in the first place? It must be something to do with work—the Camarras' weekend parties were prestigious mainly because they always furthered already glittering careers. If Christie herself was there to have close discussions about this role in *Tigresse*, Jared must also have an important career move to make while he was under this famous roof.

But what?

Well, he was a director, so it must have something to do with——

Suddenly, she remembered her conviction that Mike and Millie knew about her previous, passionate involvement with Jared. Her mind started to work with slow, dawning horror.

Was it possible that Mike and Millie Camarra were thinking of making *Tigresse* a Jared Buchanan picture? *Tigresse*, the film in which they had already approached her to take the lead role? Was that what this was all about? To throw them together and see if they could work as director and actress on *Tigresse*?

That part was perfect for her. It would put the seal of absolute bankability at the box-office on her stardom. It was everything she had been looking for in a film role, and the one man in all the world who would never, ever give her that role was Jared Buchanan...

'Oh, my God!' she muttered hoarsely, and got to her feet.

Suddenly, she was pacing the oak-panelled floor.

Playing the part of the Tigresse was the role she had dreamed of all her life. It was her Hamlet, and would prove to the world that she was an actress to be taken seriously. As soon as she read the script, she knew it was what she had been working towards all her life: the chance to act, really act, and play a woman who looked exactly like her on the outside, but was her complete opposite on the inside. Not just that, but the whole steamy ambience of the film was perfect for her. The lush settings, the sensuality, the clever quick-fire lines, the moments alone when Lelie planned and plotted, the close-ups showing her true inner thoughts, then the turn of her head to smile and lie and cheat the man she would be cast opposite...

Christie had always wanted to be a famous movie-star, but she knew that famous blonde movie-stars were two a penny. Good actresses were hard to come by, especially in the medium of film, where every flicker of expression counted for so very much in those tell-tale close-ups. The role of Tigresse would undoubtedly set her among the top, most respected leading ladies and she had to have it, she just had to have it...

Her blue eyes darted around the beautiful Spanish-style room, with its rich wood-panelled floor, the fan whirring overhead, the vast white bed littered with expensive pillows, and the antique dressing-table, three-mirrored, standing elegantly beside the vast French-windowed balcony.

It was suddenly a prison to her.

She needed to get out, to think, to think, to think...

Striding purposefully to the open doors on to the balcony, she stepped out, her sensual body moving with the wild, animal sex appeal for which she was famous, blonde hair a tousled mane around her bare shoulders, the white satin dress she wore looking more like a slinky slip on her lushly slender curves as her mind shouted, I have to have that role, I have to!

A movement beside her made her jump.

Jared had stepped out on to his balcony right beside hers.

There was an electrifying silence as they studied each other.

Ambition flew from her grasp as though she had stumbled and dropped it. All she could see or feel or think of was Jared Buchanan, and how gorgeous he looked, like a dark god standing there before her with anger in his jet-black eyes, reminding her so much of their last, terrible row.

Her voice was husky as she said, 'Hello, Jared.'

'Hello, Christie.' He was studying her as an angry lover should, and she was reacting as though they'd never been apart, her body tingling under the hard caress of his eyes. It seemed only yesterday that they had made love. She could almost taste his skin. 'Very long time no see. But it seems fate has thrown us together again.'

'Fate?' It was difficult to sound casual when your voice was shaking. 'You mean you had nothing to do with it?'

'You don't seriously think I'd want to meet up with you again under such intimate circumstances, do you?'

'Perish the thought!' Pain burned her heart like fire and it hurt even more to pretend she didn't care. 'But I think it's fairly clear that somebody not only wanted us to meet up, but knew we had once been involved. Millie Camarra seemed to know about us. I didn't tell her, so——'

'You're right, she does know, and I know who told her.' Jared raked a strong hand through his black hair. 'It was me—indirectly. I told Mike Camarra I had known you in the past, and that you might not be able to work with me because of it. I had to tell him. I suggested you for the lead role in *Tigresse*, and——'

'Oh, God...!' She caught her breath audibly, whitening. 'Then I was right about the reason you're here! You are going to direct!'

'Naturally. I found the script. The whole picture is my baby.'

She struggled to look professional, but her hands were clinging to the hot metal balcony rail, fingers damp and white-knuckled, and her mind was starting to shout again, I must have that role, I must have it, I must! But her beautiful pink pouting mouth said, 'It's an excellent script. Lots of fast scenes. Great locations.'

'And an exceptional lead role for any ambitious young actress with her eye on Hollywood immortality!'

'What's wrong with ambition, Jared?' Her blue eyes flashed angrily to his. 'What's wrong with wanting Hollywood immortality?'

'Nothing,' he drawled tightly. 'Except that you're going to have to get it through me.'

The threat was blatant. Christie lifted her head, trying to appear up to the challenge, but she knew deep inside that this one was going to hurt, this one was going to make or break her. She had fought for stardom, fought for great roles in the past—but this role was different. This was her key to Hollywood's Hall of Fame, and the man she had to fight for it was a man she loved ... but who hated her.

There was a tense silence as they took each other's measure.

Suddenly, Jared's eyes flashed down to her left hand. 'I see the newspapers didn't exaggerate about the size of that diamond! I just wonder what took you so long to make it public.'

'I don't understand what you——'

'Come off it!' he laughed harshly. 'You and Simon Mordant were lovers three years ago! Good God, you left me for him!'

'But I didn't leave you for Simon!' Her eyes flashed with furious emotion. 'Don't try to ease your own guilty conscience by blaming it all on him! I left you because you deliberately stood in the way of my——'

'Ambition?'

There was a brief silence. The warm breeze lifted strands of Jared's dark hair as he watched her with narrowed, judgemental eyes.

'Still your favourite word, Chris?'

She looked away at the sea and said, 'Ambition isn't a word—it's a character defect. They put it in you at birth and you have to spend the rest of your life trying to get it out. What was it you used to say, Jared? Something about deprivation being the mother of ambi——'

'We don't have time for a trip down memory lane! Let's just get straight to the point—how the hell we're going to work together on *Tigresse*.'

Stung by his curt dismissal, she lifted her hand and said tightly, 'I'd work with Godzilla himself for that particular role!'

'Oh, yes, you'll do anything for fame and fortune, won't you, Chris?'

'I'll even smile at you.'

He laughed harshly. 'And that role will make you the biggest star in Hollywood. It's perfect for you.' Malice glittered in his eyes. 'One might almost be forgiven for believing it was your life story!'

Her lashes flickered, her face going white as she stared at him with appalled blue eyes. 'My life story...?' Her voice was rough. 'What do you mean—my life story!'

'Well, let's examine the character of Lelie for a moment,' he said tightly. 'Here we have an amoral beauty who uses her sex appeal to further her career, destroying every man she meets, her ultimate goal nothing more or less than money, power and fame. That's you, isn't it, my darling? You're not just suited to the role—you *are* the Tigresse!'

CHAPTER TWO

FOR a second she couldn't move or speak, breathless with pain at the reality of his true opinion of her. He seriously believed what he had just said. He really thought she was the living image of Lelie. All these years, she had gone on with her career, working harder and harder, hoping he would see every milestone of achievement—and hoping deep inside that he would begin to respect her. It had always been one of her worst fears, the whole time she was with him: that he only saw her as a stupid, struggling little nobody actress, and could not possibly respect her as an equal. Love should explode all barriers—class, background and status—but, all too often, they exploded love instead.

Christie had believed Jared would, if nothing else, come to respect her professionally.

But this…this went beyond all her fears into the realm of nightmare. She couldn't bear to think that for three years Jared had looked at her name in lights and thought, There goes Christie McCall, the amoral little whore I once had an affair with.

'I'm nothing like that woman,' Christie said in a shaken voice, breathless with pain. 'Nothing, Jared. If you think back to when we first met, I'm sure you'll see that——'

'I see only that you used me as a casting couch,' he cut in harshly. 'Or at least—you tried to.'

She swayed as though he had struck her, ambition sliding from her grasp again as pain stabbed her heart. 'How can you say that?'

'A pity it didn't work,' he continued unpleasantly. 'My proposal of marriage put paid to your ambitious little plans. But you win some, you lose some. And Simon Mordant certainly proved more than happy to play on the casting couch with you. Successfully, too, as——'

'He's my agent!' she said hoarsely. 'He's supposed to help me with my work as an actress!'

'And marrying him is a very strategic career move.'

'I love Simon!'

'How very convenient for the press office.' His smile was cutting. 'A lot more convenient than the nasty little stories going the rounds two years ago.'

She caught her breath.

'Or were they just to find the right image for you? The public never can make up their mind whether they prefer a madonna to a——'

'Those stories were lies!' she said unsteadily, appalled to think he had believed them. A series of juicy tabloid scandals accusing Christie of having betrayed Simon by taking another lover, a famous producer, in order to work her way up the ladder a little faster. She had always found it hard to believe that newspapers really did just tell lies sometimes. No smoke without fire, she had always thought. But after the explosion of fake gossip two years ago, she had simply stopped believing any-thing she read, unless it was verified on television with live footage and twenty reliable witnesses—and even then she had her doubts. 'Not one word of those stories was true!'

'If they were lies—why didn't you sue?'

'I was advised not to.' She stared at him. 'Come on, Jared! You know as well as I do that a lawsuit just drags the bad publicity on for months. A dignified silence is the only way to rise above it.'

'You can play the injured innocent till you're blue in the face,' he said thickly, looking away from her, his mouth hard, 'but it won't change the fact that your engagement to Simon is just another career move.'

'I love Simon.'

'You're no more in love with him than you were with me!'

She paled, lowered her gaze, unable to reply honestly to that, because she had been desperately in love with Jared, completely in love, consumed by love, and had never forgotten him, never would, not even when he was standing there, three years later, saying the most awful, unforgivable things to her. How could he say them…how could he even think them?

Eventually, she said, 'Simon's worth ten of you!'

'Shouldn't that be ten more pictures?'

Her head came up furiously. 'He's my friend! He loves me! He understands why I need to be famous, and he always has—which is more than I can say for you! If I'm marrying him now, it's because he taught me exactly what love is. It's kindness, understanding and sharing similar needs. Simon and I have all of that, but you and I never did, did we, Jared? All we shared was a bed. I was nothing more to you than a woman you could have sex with when you had time off from your own precious career.' She raked him with hurt, angry eyes. 'And you have the nerve to call me amoral!'

'Interesting. That's exactly what I think of you. Funny how two people can see the same story from different sides of the fence, isn't it? Or should I say, different sides of the bed!'

'Oh!' She was swimming with rage. 'Oh, I don't believe you said that! How can you justify it? Accusing me of wanting nothing from you but sex!'

'When I came home at night, you were always ready, willing and able.'

'To please you, you swine!' she muttered hoarsely, trying to keep the unbelievable sting of tears from really taking hold. 'To keep you happy, make you love me more, make you want to stay with me and not look around for someone else! I was so aware of my own shortcomings that seduction seemed the only way to make you stay, Jared, and love me even though I——'

'I don't want to talk about the past,' he said thickly, turning away to stare out to sea with bleak eyes.

She studied his hard profile, saw the muscle jerking in his cheek. 'It wasn't just that I wanted to make up for my own shortcomings,' she heard herself say, trying to keep her voice strong. 'It was also because of the strain you were living under. All that work at the editing suite. You needed lovemaking to help you unwind. That's why I was always so eager, initiating lovemaking——'

'I said I didn't want to talk about the past!'

Christie shut up, biting her lip, aware she had said too much.

She couldn't believe she'd said it at all. Was that her talking? Christie the career girl, the golden girl, the girl who had to have the role of Tigresse and would do anything for it? Where was she now, and who was this passionate woman, standing white and vulnerable before her former lover, wanting nothing more than his love—and prepared to humble herself with honest declarations to get it.

Maybe he's right, she thought bitterly. We shouldn't talk about the past. Look how it's all spilling out of me, all the love, the anger, the memories of a passionate love that crashed on the rocks of ambition.

'We're here for the weekend,' Jared said tightly, 'but we're here as professionals—not ex-lovers. If we have any hope of making this film together, we'll be best served by never discussing the past.'

She swallowed hard. 'If you can manage it, Jared, so can I.'

'I'm prepared to work with you on *Tigresse*, because I know you'll be superb in the role.'

Her blue eyes flickered up, ambition sparkling at the mention of *Tigresse*, mingling with hot tears, the loss of love.

'But I'm the director, I'm the one in control, and what I say goes. Any trouble with you while I'm here, and I'll just re-cast. Got it?'

'Got it,' she said thickly, realising she had to seem strong even if she wanted to crumple up and cry. 'No trouble, no talk of the past, everything civilised and very Hollywood—even if there are undercurrents seething between us night and day! Yes, I can do that, Jared. If I must.'

His smile savaged her. 'The consummate professional!'

She stared at him with silent, bitter resentment.

'But bear in mind,' he said tightly, 'that you don't officially have the part yet. I might just decide to re-cast anyway if you're not as nice as pie to me. In fact—I think you'd better be very honest and above board while we're here.'

'I'm always honest and above board. You're the one who goes around lying to himself as well as others!'

'What was that?'

'Nothing.' She lifted her head, face strong.

He contemplated her for a second, then said, 'So, you'd better just drop the Little Miss Muffet act and be yourself. If we're going to work together in the future, it'd better be with a clean slate.'

'I quite agree.'

'Good.' He nodded, his features implacable. 'Then while we have this heaven-sent opportunity to cut away the dead wood, I suggest we use it.'

Christie blinked rapidly. 'But...you just said you didn't want to talk about the past!'

'Not right at this moment. I still haven't recovered from the horrifying shock of finding you here for the whole weekend with me!'

'Horrifying shock,' she said hoarsely, her mouth shaking. 'Yes, of course. How stupid of me. How unclean you must feel, just standing here talking to——'

'No need for melodrama,' he replied tightly. 'I think we both know the truth of what happened between us, and why I feel as angry with you as I do. But that anger will lessen if we can manage to get together over this weekend, once I've come to terms with your presence here, and have some kind of civilised discussion about——'

'How can we have a civilised discussion,' she asked in a low, angry voice, 'if you keep trying to tell me I'm an amoral whore who used you?'

'Because that's what you are,' he bit out thickly. 'And before this weekend is over, you *will* have admitted it to me.'

'Oh, for God's sake!'

'No, for your sake.' His eyes were ruthless. 'You do want this film, don't you? I mean—you do want to play the lead role in *Tigresse*, don't you?'

She stared at him, her eyes suddenly as mutinous as they were hurt. That golden prize was dancing before her again: Lelie, *Tigresse*, best actress Oscar...it blurred before her eyes, but she still wanted it, had to have it, because everything would be all right if it was hers. It was a stupid thing to believe, but she did; she just did, and always would.

'Well?' he demanded, lifting that arrogant dark head. 'Do you want the role or not?'

Her mouth shook with anger, an anger she kept in check by sheer dint of long professionalism. 'Yes!' she clipped out thickly. 'Yes, I do want the role!'

'Then you'll do as I say!' he told her under his breath.

She said nothing, but she was appalled by the implications of what he was saying, and the demands he might make of her before he agreed to cast her in *Tigresse*, and give her the chance of that glittering, golden prize.

'After dinner,' Jared said, eyes narrowing on her face. 'We'll talk after dinner. Maybe a long walk on the beach. Somewhere no one else can overhear our conversation.' He glanced at the watch on his hair-roughened wrist. 'In the meantime, I haven't even unpacked. I'll see you at dinner. And you'd better be ready to confess to being exactly like Lelie, or you won't be starring in *Tigresse* next year.'

Turning on his heel, he strode off the balcony, leaving Christie just standing there, trembling from head to foot.

She was alone on the balcony, and the sun was hot on her face, but all the glittering prizes in the world could not save her now as she felt success turn to ashes in her hands, stripping her of fame and power, leaving her nothing but a woman—in love with a man who hated her.

The warm breeze lifted strands of her blonde hair. She moved her head gently to let them slide down her back, and a second later she was back in the past, twenty-five years old, innocent and in love with nothing but her career, standing in that little newsagent's shop in Elstree High Street while a tall, dark-haired stranger stared at her across the greetings cards rack...

'Hi!' He had followed her out of the shop, measuring his long stride to her shorter one. 'I hear the newsagent's daughter is having an affair with the baker's son.'

'Everybody knows about that!' She had laughed. 'You must be new in town!'

He had grimaced, laughing too. 'I only got here two weeks ago. I thought it was hot news.'

'Two weeks ago?' Christie had tucked her Mars bar into her handbag, frowning thoughtfully as she allowed the very handsome stranger to follow her and chat her up. 'You're not working on the Jared Buchanan picture, are you? Over at the film studios?'

'Yes, as a matter of fact, I am.' Those dark eyes made her pulse skip beats. 'Why? Interested in movies?'

'Of course!' She had smiled shyly at him, unaccustomed to being so wildly and instantly attracted to a man. 'I'm an actress.'

He had stopped walking then, looking down at her in cool silence. Christie stopped too. It seemed natural. He was so gorgeous, and if he was threatening it was only in a very exciting way. The leather jacket and jeans he wore made her like him even more. She hated vain, strutting men, met so many of them in her profession. This man was so masculine and unpretentious that she assumed he was a cameraman, or some other behind-the-cameras kind of guy. Laid back at the same time as being dynamic, well spoken without being upper class, and as for those dark, passionate eyes...

'What kind of actress?'

'I'm in a soap.' She had smiled, shrugging, almost ashamed of it because of the bad press soaps always got. 'At Elstree, just across the road from you. I play Lucy Bellamy in *Bellamy Place*.'

'I'm afraid I don't watch TV. Are you well known?'

'Only if you watch soaps!' she had laughed. 'But it's a good career rung and, besides, I like living and working here for the moment.'

A smile touched the hard mouth. 'So you'd know about the social life in Elstree? I'm completely lost—don't know where anything is; nightclubs, restaurants, that kind of thing.'

'Well...' She shrugged again. 'I'm afraid I don't go out much in the evenings. Everything revolves around work.'

'Don't you even know where I could get a good meal at night?'

She thought for a second. 'The King's Head is supposed to be good.'

'Great.' The dark eyes had sparkled so charmingly at her that she had felt breathless. 'Why don't you have dinner with me there tonight?'

A hot flush of excited attraction had burned her face. 'Oh...yes, I suppose I could...well, thank you...' She had looked away, aware she was stammering like a schoolgirl and embarrassed by her own shyness.

He had smiled, saying deeply, 'I'll meet you there at seven-thirty.' Then he had touched her hot cheek with one strong hand and walked coolly across the road leaving her pulses racing with awareness of that touch.

She thought of nothing else for the rest of the day. The girls at the studios teased her mercilessly, aware she was mooning over a man for the first time in their long acquaintance with her, and delighted she had at least 'joined the rest of us by meeting someone gorgeous'! Christie had almost enjoyed their teasing: the handsome stranger was definitely worth it, and besides, mooning over a man was such a new experience to her that she savoured every moment of it.

All her life, she had thought of nothing but her career. Men had asked her out, of course, but she had rarely accepted dates with them, and on the one occasion when she had found herself alone with a man at night, she had almost been forced into bed on a 'date-rape'. Escaping that with nothing but a few unpleasant fumblings followed by a struggle, she hadn't wanted to get close to a man again. That was four years ago, though, and this was now. She couldn't wait to see her handsome cameraman again.

But he was no cameraman, as she found out when she walked towards the King's Head, saw a long black limousine pull up outside it, and watched her handsome stranger step out, still in jeans and leather jacket.

'Hey!' A man in the rear of the limo called out. 'Jared—what about your wake-up call?'

He strode back to the car, and bent to the window. 'Keep it at five a.m. I might be busy, but I doubt it. She doesn't seem that kind of girl and, besides, we're over budget as it is. We have to stick to schedule.'

'OK, Jared. You're the director.'

Christie caught her breath as she heard those words, and stumbled out of the shadows into the glowing light of the fish and chip shop next to the pub.

Jared turned, seeing her.

There was a long, stunned silence. The pub sign creaked over the white steps, cars drove past in the cold night, red tail lights flashing hot in the January air.

'You're Jared Buchanan?' Christie had whispered.

His mouth hardened. He patted the roof of the limo, pushed away from it, and strode coolly over to Christie, his hands shoved deep in the pockets of his dark jacket.

'Does it make any difference?'

'Of course it makes a difference!' Her eyes were appalled. 'My God, you must know it does, or you would have told me sooner.'

'Would I?' A dark regret filled his eyes as he shrugged. 'I'm not so sure. It's so rare that I'm taken on face value. Most people I meet just see dollars and cents when they look at me. As for beautiful young actresses...' His mouth twisted cynically. 'You can imagine what they see.'

Christie looked into his hard face and struggled to overcome the sense of inferiority that was swamping her.

'I get so sick of it,' he said deeply. 'Everybody wants to use me to further their own careers. Sometimes I dream about meeting people who've never heard of me or my work.'

'You could go and live in Outer Mongolia,' she had said with a shy smile.

He touched her cheek. 'Or I could have dinner with you.'

Christie leapt with response, her heart pounding. 'Oh but...I know who you are now. It wouldn't be the same. I thought you were just a handsome cameraman, someone I could——'

'Be yourself with?'

She had nodded slowly, flushing.

'Then carry on thinking of me like that,' he had said softly, taking her hand. 'And let me be myself with you.'

So they went into the pub together, took an intimate table in the shadows in the corner, and ate steak and kidney pie washed down with lager and lime. Christie still felt inferior to him every time she remembered with a shock that she was dining with Jared Buchanan. But most of the time, he was right: they were able to forget and pretend and just be themselves without thinking of power or prestige or fame.

Later, he walked her home along the cold, dark streets.

'I suppose you'll go off me,' she said sadly, her arm linked through his, leaning her head against his broad shoulder as they ambled along, 'and never want to see me again, if I tell you I want to be famous.'

'No.' He had had a smile in his voice. 'I won't go off you.'

'It's what I've always dreamed of. My name in lights...' Her eyes had flickered up to the dark sky. 'I want to be like them. See? They live above the rest of the world, and nobody can hurt them, because they're just too far away.'

He had slipped his arm around her, turning her, saying deeply, 'I live up there, Chris, and it's not what I thought it would be.'

'People who get there always say that.'

'That's because it's true.'

Her hands had slipped so naturally around his strong neck. 'All clichés are true. But we have to find that out for ourselves, don't we?'

'The only cliché I can think of right now is—kiss me...' His dark head moved down slowly as his arms tightened around her, giving her time to get away, but she couldn't do anything other than raise her mouth to meet his and, when the kiss came, it was a love song.

The world spun on its axis, her mouth was opening beneath his and her eyes were closed before she knew what was happening, letting that tender kiss turn so rapidly to fire, to real passion, the onslaught so deep and fast that they were both helpless in the grip of fierce excitement as they clung together beneath the cold, distant glitter of the stars.

'I knew it would be like this...' he muttered hoarsely against her mouth, his breathing as ragged as his heartbeat. 'I thought about it all day—tell me you did, too.'

'All day...' she moaned breathlessly through bruised lips.

'Let me come into your flat and kiss you some more!'

She stiffened in his arms. 'No...'

He closed his eyes and said thickly, 'Chris, please...I won't try anything, I promise. But I don't want to go home yet. I want to be with you some more. Just a cup of coffee and a long kiss. That's all I——'

'Look,' she said huskily, 'I don't know you well enough yet, and it may seem all right now, but how would it look in court if anything went wrong? "Yes, m'lud, I let a stranger come into my flat and——"'

'All right,' he said with a wry grimace. 'I see your point, even if it is a little insulting. It's a man's world, we built it, we run it, and we have to pay the price for the men who take advantage of it.'

Christie had laughed, but it had been the first sign of his out-and-out chauvinism, and she should have been warned.

'So...' He had touched her cheek. 'I'll let you go tonight, but only if you promise to see me tomorrow night.'

She promised, and their love-affair began.

They became inseparable very quickly. For the first week they were with each other every night, but he left her at her front door and did not go further than a long kiss under the stars. But gradually her trust grew, and they began to spend evenings at home together, always at her place, and always accompanied by long, long kisses interspersed with deep conversation.

'Did you always want to be famous, Jared?'

'Always. I believed everything would be all right if I could just have enough power, fame and money. But it doesn't solve any of the old problems.'

'What were the old problems?' She had held her breath as she asked him that, lying in the lamplight of her front room, entwined on the sofa with him, afraid to tell him of her background and her own reasons for wanting fame.

'I'm an orphan. I was orphaned at birth and put in a home.'

She stared, and didn't breathe for several seconds.

'It made me angry,' he said deeply. 'Living in that awful orphanage with all those other lost boys, and no Wendy to look after us.'

'Oh, my love...'

'I used to lie awake at night and dream of a real mother, what she'd look like, how she'd cook for me, and how she'd love me. I'd fall asleep smiling, then wake up to find myself being dragged out of bed by the nearest bully, and I'd know I was back in the real world, having to fight just to keep my position in the lost-boy hierarchy.'

Understanding lit her soul as she whispered, 'And you'd think to yourself: when I'm famous, no one will dare do this to me.'

He had laughed ruefully. 'Childish, I know, but——'

'It's the way it takes root,' she had nodded, stroking his dark hair. 'Just as it did in me...' And, finally, she was able to tell him about her own childhood, feeling the inexpressible relief that someone understood.

'Do you think you'll ever get there?' Jared asked her. 'Up in the sky with the stars?'

'I...' She had floundered then, suddenly reminded of his towering professional status compared to her, and so she had just laughed and said, 'Maybe. Who knows? But what does it matter tonight? I'm in love, and everything's all right so long as you're here.'

Everything was all right, too. She felt loved for the first time in her life, and the previously forbidden world of close personal intimacy was opening up to her with every second she spent in Jared's company. It did not change her ambitions; it just added a new dimension to her life.

One of the most powerful dimensions was that of the senses.

Jared's long kisses on the couch were turning into passionate sessions that were getting closer and closer to full lovemaking. Night after night they lay together touching, kissing, exploring each other's bodies. He was teaching her the true meaning of desire—and of frustration.

Eventually, neither of them could go on without consummating their love, but it was Jared who finally halted the crazed frustration they were living with and brought them into the final dimension of love.

'I can't go on like this much longer...' he said hoarsely as they lay semi-naked together one night on the couch, both sheened in sweat and panting with pent-up desire. 'Darling, I know you're scared, but we're almost there, and I really am reaching the end of my tether.'

'So am I,' she had moaned against his hot neck, the ache between her thighs so consuming she could feel the blood pounding round her body, racing hard and fast to that engorged nub of flesh and the slippery heat below it. 'I think I'm going to explode if I don't surrender soon!'

'Surrender tonight,' he had urged with a deep groan, and she had whispered yes, which made him groan even more as he kissed her, then swept her into his arms and carried her to the dark bedroom, laid her down on the bed, and took her into fulfilment by slowly stripping her naked, stroking her, whispering wicked words of love to her, his own powerful naked body moving slowly against her without entering her. His expertise left her a quivering wreck of flesh beneath him as she went into climax, gasping hoarsely in disbelief.

'It won't hurt so much now, darling,' Jared told her hoarsely as he entered her, but when his rigid manhood pushed against the barrier of her virginity he gave a rough cry, lost control and thrust into her hard, fast, shaking from head to foot as he went into violent climax.

Christie just lay beneath him in stunned silence. Was it supposed to hurt like that? And be over so quickly? Her own pleasure was still pulsing through her body, but she had expected his to last longer.

'I'm sorry...' Jared had groaned in abject horror as he lifted his head, gasping for breath. 'I was so excited I couldn't stop myself... but if you knew how it felt to feel you... inside... a real virgin. Chris, I've dreamed of it all my life. I didn't fall in love with you because you were a virgin, but it does make it all perfect.'

She found out later what he meant by that: that virgins made perfect wives.

But at the time, she just loved him all the more for saying it, because it helped stem the feelings of inferiority which were growing steadily, not only because he was so powerful and famous, but also because he was quite the most experienced lover she could have encountered.

After that first night, he never lost control so fast again, and his expertise in lovemaking was almost frightening. They made love night after night, endlessly, and she learnt what multiple orgasm really meant as Jared unleashed the full power of his sexual experience on her shaking, untutored, wildly responsive body.

He asked her to move in with him; she did.

They became closer than ever, and sometimes she wondered what he saw in her, but he was so devoted and so loving that she didn't have time to dwell on it, and when she did it made her so frightened of losing him that she had no option other than to push the thoughts away before they wrecked her confidence, and pray that their relationship would lead to marriage.

He proposed when she least expected it.

They were in the beautiful, dazzling kitchen of his apartment. She was ironing his shirts for him, something she'd taken to doing lately, just for the sheer romantic novelty of it. Jared was watching her from the kitchen table, smiling, his eyes loving.

'I might fire the housekeeper tomorrow,' he said lightly. 'What would you think of that?'

She had laughed, ironing the crisp white sleeve. 'Oh...I don't think I'd have time to do this every day, darling.'

'Not even when we're married?'

Christie had almost burnt a hole in the shirt, staring at him as her hand went temporarily motionless, and her mind went clean of all thought.

'I'm asking you to marry me,' he had said huskily. 'Please say you will...'

'Of course I will!' she had whispered, and a second later they were in each other's arms, holding tight, so tight, as love enfolded them and kept them both free from harm forever.

He had already bought the ring; a beautiful emerald so dazzling she could barely stand to look at it without feeling a powerful mixture of love and inadequacy.

'I'm a very traditional man,' Jared said as he slid it on her finger. 'I want a big white wedding, a long honeymoon and a new home to move into as soon as we start married life. But with my schedule at the studio—I won't be free to do that until August this year.'

'I can wait another five months,' she had laughed joyfully. 'And I want a traditional wedding, too. Bridesmaids, bouquets—the lot!'

'And children?' he had asked deeply, his eyes intense.

'Lots of children.' Tears filled her eyes as she buried her face in his neck. 'Hundreds of them. All the living image of you. And I'll call them all Jared. Jared the Second, the third, the fourth——'

'You want them right away?' he had said urgently.

'Well...' She had hesitated, suddenly aware that, no, she did not want them right away. In fact, she didn't want them for another four or five years. Not until she was thirty, not until she was famous, not until she had that special place in the sky where no one could ever hurt her again.

'Darling?' He waited, his body tense, and suddenly she was aware that he was afraid to look at her, just as she was afraid to look at him, both of them anxious that they had finally reached the one flaw in their future plans, and neither wanting to admit it; to have that argument.

'Jared,' she had said carefully. 'I do want children. Lots of them. But just not right away. I'm not really ready yet.'

Silence.

She felt very tense, and said quickly, 'I want to be famous, remember? A famous actress, high in the stars, name in lights...' She pulled back to look at him with wary eyes. 'Give me time to see if I can make it. Then, if I really can't do it as well as you have—well, I'll accept it and have children with you.'

His dark lashes had flickered as he gave a false smile. 'Yes, of course. But do you really think you'll make it? I mean—you are twenty-five, darling. Most stars are at least living in Hollywood by the time they're your age, if not already world-famous.'

It was her turn to give a false smile. 'Maybe you're right.'

The next day, she met Simon Mordant.

CHAPTER THREE

THE hot Californian sun was glittering across the distant sea like yellow diamonds strewn across its blue waters. Palm trees waved softly in the warm breeze.

We should have had that argument right there and then, Christie thought, remembering it all. Everything started to go wrong from that point. It was all there, underneath the surface, right from the moment we met, but that was when it really started to show itself, and that was when we should have talked honestly about the future.

But they hadn't wanted to wreck something so perfect by bringing reality into the picture.

So they had carried on, still in love with each other, but hiding their true feelings from one another step by step, inch by inch, neither wanting to be the one to provoke that terrible argument they both knew was now on the cards.

She herself had felt bitterly resentful of Jared, knowing he was only paying lip-service to her career dreams, but of course she couldn't say anything to him without looking a fool. After all—he was a famous award-winning director. He would have good reason to laugh in her face if she tried to claim equality in dreams of stardom. Even though he knew why she needed it so badly. The facts were that he had it, and she didn't. So how could she discuss it with him any more? All they were able to talk about now was love, sex and their forthcoming marriage plans.

And once Simon entered the picture, he gave Christie that shot-in-the-arm-confidence she so badly needed. Simon believed in her. Simon talked endlessly of her talent and her drive. Simon photographed her from every angle, took video footage of her acting scenes from plays, from films, and he sent those photos and videos to his contacts in Hollywood on a regular basis.

At first, Christie had tried to tell Jared how closely she was working with Simon. But he just became aggressive and accused Simon of trying to get Christie into bed. So, after a while, it seemed easier to avoid the arguments, the shouting and the jealous scenes by just not talking about Simon whenever possible. Simon was the first person in a long time who had really believed she could get into films and was not only prepared to help her, but actually had the contacts to do so. How could she possibly stop seeing him?

By this time it was April, and Jared was editing his film. He was at the editing suite sometimes for two or three days at a time, not even bothering to come home at night. Although she missed him dreadfully, it did give her a chance to work even harder with Simon in Jared's absence. And besides, when Jared did come home, he never wanted to do anything other than make love.

He had fired the housekeeper in March, and Christie had been expected to take over where she had left off. At first it was quite easy—the house was already spick and span. But gradually the dust began to grow on the skirting boards, the food began to disappear from the well-stocked fridge, and the washing began to pile up.

Not only did Christie have to work ten hours a day, six days a week at Elstree—still keeping her relationship with Jared Buchanan a complete secret from the girls and the British Press—but she also had to put in a lot of hard work after hours with Simon Mordant.

How could she possibly cope with housework on top of all that? It had been wonderful fun at first, but it had really only been play-acting for Jared's benefit, and when he was no longer there to smile lovingly as he watched her cook his dinner, clean the floor or iron his shirts—the novelty faded into drudgery.

No matter how many times she made the bed, it always got unmade the next day. Going shopping in the supermarket was next to impossible, given that she only had an hour for lunch every day, and was frequently too tired to want to trundle about with a trolley in a packed supermarket, queue up with other harassed shoppers, and then trudge home with heavy shopping bags that almost broke her arms. As for washing and ironing Jared's shirts...well, she became slapdash to say the least.

Of course, he noticed, and they began to have rows about the housework when really, they should have been talking about the central issue: that she wanted to be a famous actress and he wanted her to be a wife and mother.

She decided that she would make him so happy with her as a woman that he forgot all about her inadequacies as a housewife. So she went out in her lunch-break the next day to buy some silky, sexy lingerie. But when Jared came home that night to find her waiting for him in black bra, black silk briefs, black stockings and a red garter belt, he lost his temper, they had a terrible row, and he ended up calling her a whore.

She was so hurt and angry that she slapped him across the face, but his reaction was to jerk her hard against him and slap her rear in return. One thing led to another, and before they both knew it, they were fiercely aroused, making angry love on the floor.

Christie didn't wear black lingerie again, but she did seduce him frequently when he got back from the studios, because it made her feel more his equal than she had done in the whole course of their relationship, and besides—sex was now the one area where they could communicate honestly.

In June, the whole thing came to a head.

Simon had got her a screen test with Camarra Pictures.

'I have to fly to Los Angeles tomorrow!' Christie had told Jared with a combination of fear and excitement. 'They're testing me for a bit-part, but it could lead to a contract if I'm good enough.'

'What...!' Jared had stared at her in shocked fury. 'But what about us? I'm almost through with editing this picture! I thought we were going to start a family——'

'Jared, I told you I needed to do this,' she had said in a low voice. 'And you agreed to wait for children until I'd at least had a shot at Hollywood.'

'I didn't expect you to go through with it! I thought you'd just gradually accept your limitations and give up dreams of stardom!'

Christie had been so hurt and angry that the bubble of pretence just burst as it all came tumbling out and she found herself shouting at him that he was a male chauvinist pig, that he'd always looked down on her, never believed in her talent, never really loved or understood her, just wanted to turn her into a clockwork doll to cook and clean for him.

'It's because I love you that I won't let you do this!' Jared had shouted back, red in the face with rage. 'Hollywood will destroy you, you're not tough enough for it—or talented enough!'

'Oh, you rotten swine!' She had been incoherent with pain and pent-up resentment. 'You've always despised me, haven't you! All those lies about how talented I was, how I was going to make it to the stars!'

'What about your lies! All those nights talking about our children, our happy home—and, as for the big seduction scenes night after night, my God, I should have known I was being manipulated!'

The row escalated.

They were helpless to stop it, all the secret resentments pouring out as they shouted at one another, tearing each other to pieces.

In the end, Jared shouted, 'If you go to Los Angeles with Simon Mordant tomorrow—we're finished!'

'All right, then!' she had shouted back. 'We're finished!'

And she had pushed past him in blind fury, striding into the hall, wrenching open the front door and walking out of his life forever, not even bothering to take her few possessions with her. Jared didn't try to stop her. He strode furiously after her along the hall and slammed the door shut as she left.

She never saw him again.

She flew to LA the next day, took her screen test, and was lucky enough to find herself accepted. She told herself she'd one day stop crying herself to sleep over Jared.

But she never forgot him. All along the road to success, she never stopped thinking of him. Every time a picture was released, she'd think, Jared will see this, and he'll start to respect me. Every time her face was on a magazine cover, she'd think, Jared will see this at a newsstand in LA or New York, Paris or London, and he'll begin to admire me.

Why did it hurt so much that he hadn't?

Because I'm still in love with him, she realised, and then the tears began to slip out over her lashes, rolling hotly down her cheeks as she stood on that beautiful balcony in California.

I mustn't cry out here, she told herself. Jared might see, and he mustn't know that I still love him, because if he does, he'll know he has even greater power over me than he does already. For no matter how badly he hurts me, I must have the role, must have it...

Turning, she went back into her room.

It was seven o'clock now, and she had to get ready for dinner. This was a business weekend, after all. She was expected to look like a movie-star, behave like a golden girl, even if her heart was breaking into tiny pieces and her whole world was falling apart.

Quickly, she unpacked, then showered and blow-dried her long hair into the sensual, tousled mane she was famous for. The dress was chosen carefully: a long silk Grecian masterpiece of sensuality, flowing over her slender curves to her feet, gold sandals peeping out and a gold necklace coiled at her lightly tanned throat.

Looking into the mirror, she saw a movie-star, rich with sexuality. No one would guess that inside was a hurt, vulnerable woman who had lost the only love she had ever known. What a professional, she thought with a hoarse laugh.

It was seven forty-five, and she must not delay any longer. So she left her bedroom, walked down the long corridor, and found herself on that sweeping staircase where the chandelier glittered over the marble hall and the gods and goddesses of the silver screen looked down from oil-painted immortality on another party at Casa Camarra.

She was halfway down the stairs when she heard the voices.

'Simon Mordant...' a deep throaty female voice said far below in a sophisticated New York accent. 'Long time no see!'

'Nessa...' Simon's voice was cool, austere.

Christie stopped suddenly on the staircase, frowning. They couldn't see her because they were too busy staring at each other, but she could see them and it was clear to her immediately that here was fierce attraction, anger, emotion and hatred all sizzling out invisibly between Simon Mordant and Nessa Vale.

'So how are you, Simon?' drawled the famous actress. 'You're looking good.'

'You too, Nessa. I hear you're seeing Jared Buchanan these days?'

'And you're engaged to Christie McCall!' Nessa laughed, dark eyes flashing at him. 'The blonde bimbo herself! What a surprise, Simon! It never occurred to me that you'd do an Arthur Miller! What do they call you? Not the egghead and the hourglass surely? Even Hollywood doesn't repeat its own clichés—although you obviously don't draw the line.'

Christie stared down, astonished by the venom in Nessa Vale's voice. What on earth had either she or Simon done to deserve such spite from Nessa?

'Christie and I love each other,' Simon was saying with equal anger in his voice. 'And she is not a blonde bimbo. She's a very fine actress and I'm proud to be her agent.'

Nessa Vale laughed spitefully. 'You said that about the last blonde bimbo you liaised dangerously with! What was her name, now? Oh, I forget! She disappeared from the industry after that scandalous affair you had with her!' She patted his hard cheek with one long-fingered hand. 'Never mind, darling. Maybe Christie McCall has more stamina. From what Jared's told me about her bedtime appetites, I'm sure she has!' Turning on her heel, she walked away, stunningly austere in a long black dress that fitted her tall, bony figure to perfection, and complemented her coolly aristocratic New York accent, so similar to Simon's.

Simon watched Nessa go, his eyes blazing with steely rage. 'Little bitch!' he swore hoarsely under his breath.

Christie went down the stairs, and he looked up suddenly.

'I'm sorry,' she said at once. 'I didn't overhear that deliberately. I just began to hear and was so shocked I barely knew what to do. Why on earth does she hate us both so much, Simon?'

He just stared at her as though he had never seen her before, his eyes fixed and frozen. They moved over her then, rapidly, taking in the long ivory silk Grecian dress, the sexuality of her body, the blonde hair cascading over her slender, gold-tanned shoulders, and finally coming to rest on her full rich, sultry pink mouth.

'Christie...' he said bleakly, and looked away.

In silence, she kept her hand on the end of the banister, standing in the marble hallway with him, her astonished mind beginning to grope at a quite incredible truth.

'Simon...?' Her voice was husky, shell-shocked. 'Were you involved with Nessa Vale in the past?'

He went pink, raked a hand through his ash-blond hair. 'Yes. I was——' his voice roughened '—very deeply involved with her several years ago. Just before I met you, in fact.'

She just stared at him, incredulous that he had never mentioned her name.

'I always meant to tell you,' Simon said thickly. 'But the opportunity never arose and, besides, I thought I'd never see her again.'

'With all of us living out here?' she whispered. 'All of us working in films? That's absurd and you know it.'

'All right. I thought——' He looked up at her quickly, then lowered his gaze, his mouth tightening. 'I thought I'd feel indifferent to her when we met again. Triumphant, even.'

'And what did you feel?'

He looked at her again, pain in his grey eyes, and asked under his breath in counter-challenge, 'How did you feel when you saw Jared again?'

Christie paled, looking away, pain lancing her heart.

'Right,' Simon muttered. 'It's not so easy to face the ghosts, is it? Especially not with such short notice of their appearance.'

'Simon...' She moved awkwardly to her old friend and sympathetically touched his shoulder. 'I do understand how you feel. Or, at least, I think I understand. But...' She drew an unsteady breath. 'But we're supposed to be getting married. If you're still in love with Nessa Vale, then you must——'

'I'm not in love with her!' he ground out thickly, but the blaze of passion in his normally cool, grey eyes told a different story. 'I detest the little bitch! She walked out on me, humiliated me, made me——' He broke off, his face running with betraying colour, and got his emotions under control, his mouth tightening. 'I'm sorry, I'm handling this badly,' he said, after a second. 'It's the shock of running into her unexpectedly, of hearing all that venom from her. But don't worry, Christie. I'm not in love with Nessa any more, and I fully intend to go through with my marriage to you. All right?'

'Go through with it?' She made a wry face. 'You make it sound like a prison sentence!'

'Hell, I didn't mean it to sound like that.' He slung his right arm caringly around her and squeezed her close against him for a brief moment, kissing the top of her head. 'You know I love you, darling. You know I'm sincere when I say I want to marry you. I may have a few problems dealing with Nessa over this weekend— but you mustn't let them affect our relationship. All right?'

She frowned, drawing back to look into his eyes. 'Do you think she's going to try and get at you, then? More than she did just now?'

'I'm fairly sure she will,' he responded tightly, pain in his eyes. 'But it's all in the past, remember? Everything we were saying on the drive up here still stands.'

'About dark, destructive love?' Her eyes scanned his. 'Is that who Nessa was for you, Simon? The Grand Passion? The one you can't forget?'

He gave a shaky laugh. 'I guess so. But isn't that who Jared Buchanan is for you? I mean—I'm not the only one around here who's going to have trouble this weekend from an old flame!'

She paled again, saying, 'I've already met up with him. On the balcony. I—I've had my first argument of the weekend with him. With any luck, there might not be any more. If I keep my head, don't let my feelings get the better of me.'

'Think you can manage it?' he asked, concerned.

'I can try!' she said with a bitter laugh. 'I'll just keep telling myself that old Hollywood saying! Behind every successful woman is a man who broke her heart! Come on, Simon——' she caught at his hand with a need to change the subject '—let's go out on to the terrace and start as we mean to go on: together.'

He gave a wry smile, and they strolled, hand in hand, across the marble hallway, across the ante-room, and out on to the hot stone terrace where the Californian sun still burnt bright in a halcyon blue sky while waiters moved among the guests handing out frozen margaritas.

Across by the white Roman statues and the glimmering blue pool stood Jared, magnificent in a black suit, his dark head bent to smile into Nessa Vale's eyes.

Jealousy ripped through Christie. Was it true that Jared had told Nessa terrible things about her? About how she behaved sexually? God, it didn't bear thinking of! Her hand shook as she took a frozen margarita from a passing waiter, sipping the crushed ice drink of tequila, lime juice and triple sec, struggling not to notice how close Jared stood to Nessa, or how his dark eyes moved with desire over her thin red lips.

'How long were you involved with her?' she asked, turning to Simon, turning her back on Jared so she would no longer have to see him with that other woman.

Simon looked up, his face suddenly tense and his body still.

'Simon, talk to me, please!' she said fiercely. 'I don't want to think about Jared or how close he's standing to——'

'Yes, of course.' He stared at her, blinking rapidly. 'Well, let me see now...I first met Nessa...when was it? I can't quite remember how we met or where. Or can I? Maybe I need a little time to think——'

'Dinner is served!' the tall Californian waiter boomed from the double doors which opened on to the dining-room.

People greeted this announcement with smiles and laughter and began moving towards the double doors.

'We mustn't discuss this at dinner,' Simon murmured to Christie. 'It would be disastrous if anyone overheard. But I promise you we will discuss it, some time this weekend. OK, Christie? OK?'

She gave a deep sigh. 'Fine! Just get me through this wretched weekend without any emotional traumas, and stick close to me at all times!'

'Come on, kid!' he smiled. 'Chin up! We've been though rougher times than this over the last three years! And we'll get through this weekend, so long as we re-member how much we want calm, mature love—not dark, destructive passion.'

'Yes...I must remember that at all times. All times...' Out of the corner of her eye she saw Jared moving

towards them with Nessa at his side. 'Quick! Let's go
into the dining-room before they get close to us!'

Simon smiled tensely down at her, put an elegant arm
around her slim shoulders, and rapidly led her off the
terraced pool area way ahead of Jared and Nessa.

The dining-room was as superb as the rest of the house.
Fifty-feet long with a forty-foot-high ceiling, it posi-
tively groaned under the weight of art deco chandeliers,
magnificent polished redwood-panelled walls, and a
stunning set of oil paintings of famous film stars of the
heyday of Hollywood—the twenties and thirties. Christie
noticed Greta Garbo staring enigmatically from one wall,
Marilyn Monroe incandescently beautiful on another and
Clark Gable dominating as the King of Hollywood,
dressed as Rhett Butler and leaning rakishly against a
tall white plinth.

'Everyone has a place-card with their name on it,'
Millie announced as they entered the dining-room. 'Just
look for your name and you'll find the people you're
sitting with.'

Christie's heart sank. She exchanged horrified glances
with Simon. Behind her, she sensed Jared stride into the
dining-room, narrowed eyes flicking around in search of
his place-setting. He stopped abruptly, a hard look
tightening his handsome face.

He lifted his dark head, eyes glittering with anger.
'How very thoughtful of Millie! It seems Miss McCall
is sitting beside me tonight!'

Christie caught her breath, shooting a furious look at
Millie.

'Am I sitting on the other side of you, Jared?' Nessa
asked in her icy New York voice.

But Simon was already striding angrily to the other
side of the table, staring down at the name places in the
shape of black-white clapperboards. 'No. I'm afraid I'm
your dinner partner for the evening, Nessa.'

The four of them stood there, each aware that Millie had brought them together deliberately, hoping to enjoy for herself the passionate undercurrents that would inevitably whirl out in a cross-current between the four of them, causing jealousy, rage, desire and hatred over the next forty-eight hours.

CHAPTER FOUR

ALL around them people talked, laughed and drank. Uniformed waiters poured chilled Californian Chardonnay. Gold-plated cutlery flashed under the lights and Christie wondered suddenly if she were in a film but had lost her place in the script or had been miscast, because the situation was quite beyond her.

'Christie,' Jared said sardonically, 'you'd better come and take your place beside me.' His dark eyes flicked to the others. 'I advise you two to follow suit and fall in with our hostess's wishes.'

Jared, if nothing else, knew how to behave.

Pulling herself together, Christie showed her own good manners and style as she lifted her head high, pinned a smile to her face, and walked with a sensual, unhurried sway to Jared. He gave a hard, grudging smile of admiration, his dark eyes flickering with sexual appreciation over her body as he held her chair out for her and watched her sink down on to it.

'Beautifully done,' he murmured against her ear, standing behind her, dark head bent. 'Keep it up all weekend, and the role of Lelie will be yours for the taking. Didn't I tell you you were a consummate professional?'

'No need to tell me, Jared,' she murmured tensely. 'Surely I've already proved it to the whole world?'

'Certainly with those articles about you,' he drawled, sitting down beside her. 'What's that old saying about the oldest profession in the world...?'

'I told you those stories were lies.'

'So you did.' He flicked an imaginary speck of dust from his dark cuff, a cool smile on his cynical mouth.

Christie looked at him angrily through her lashes. So this was how it would be. Impeccable behaviour in public; hostility and malice in private. And sooner or later the two would begin to spill over into each other, leaving Christie stranded on location with a film crew to watch her personal destruction at the hands of the man she loved.

'Good pre-publicity, as a matter of fact,' Jared murmured lazily, watching her, knowing he was needling her badly and enjoying every second of it. 'The Press office could work a nice little tie-in. Something about you being the perfect choice to play Lelie, because—well, just look at your personal past.'

'I wouldn't allow that kind of publicity.'

'You wouldn't be able to stop it.' His dark brows rose with cool awareness of his own power. 'And if you threaten to sue, I might even have it written into your contract.'

'I've already signed my new contract,' she countered, heart thudding fast with fear and anger, already seeing that golden, glittering prize dancing out of her reach. 'You can't tear it up and start again.'

'No, but I can fire you if you try to block my publicity machine.'

Christie sat very still, breathing hard, her hands balled into fists under the elegant table.

'Ever been fired from a picture, Chris?' Jared murmured softly in her ear. 'Course you haven't. Consummate professional like you. You'd do anything to get the part of Lelie—and anything to keep it.'

She couldn't believe how quickly this was escalating. Was he really going to demand that kind of publicity for the film, pre-release? And what else would he demand? What else . . . ?

Suddenly, the waiter was beside her, serving piping hot clam chowder from a silver tureen. She stared at it fixedly, her eyes fierce blue with shock and anger, while her mind turned over and over the question, what would she have to do to get the part of Lelie?

She didn't want to answer that. She was afraid of coming face to face with her own self-respect and finding out that she would rather be able to live with herself than join the Hollywood legends in immortality.

Marilyn Monroe was on the wall far away, smiling through a haze of blonde ambition, and Christie thought, I'll never join her on that wall if Jared brings push to shove. Maybe he had been right years ago when he'd said she wasn't tough enough for Hollywood. She certainly wasn't tough enough to fight Jared with his own weapons and win.

'What else will I demand from you?' Jared murmured smilingly beside her, one long finger stroking his hard mouth. 'Let me see...'

'For the role of Lelie?' she found her voice saying. 'Don't demand too much, Jared. I may not want to play her any more.'

'You'd kill your own grandmother to play that part!'

'As my grandmother is already dead, I think——'

'You know exactly what I mean.'

'Really? Do explain.' She sipped the chilled Chardonnay in the elegant crystal glass, but her hand was shaking.

'All right,' Jared said flatly. 'You and I both know that your ambition is the single biggest motivational force you've got. Lelie is the role that could put you at the top of the tree forever. It could win you best actress. It could make you, quite simply, into the most bankable star in Hollywood. So don't try to pretend you don't want it!'

Christie stared down at her soup. She might never achieve the fame she desired if she let Jared get to her. But then again—how could she stop him getting to her when she was quite clearly still in love with him?

'That's what you've dedicated your life to pursuing, isn't it?' Jared said tersely, watching her, unaware of her thoughts. 'Fame, fortune, a slice of immortality. Well, congratulations. It's within reach. All you have to do is——'

'Lie to you,' she cut in, looking at him bitterly. 'Tell you I'm a mercenary, manipulative little cheat with the morals of an alley cat.'

'Why not?' he said bitingly. 'It's what you are!'

Christie put her soup spoon down with a clatter, her mouth a tight, white line of rage.

'No need to be ashamed of it,' drawled Jared mockingly. 'Most men find your type of woman very exciting. And I'm no exception. I'm a man like any other—I'd enjoy taking you to bed again. Particularly now that I feel nothing but lust for that sexy little body of yours.' He laughed, eyes cynical as they flickered over her. 'I'm only too well aware that you could show me a very good time if I made it worth your while.'

'How very kind of you to say so! But if all you feel is lust—why are you being so vengeful?'

Jared's black lashes flickered, and he looked away, saying thickly, 'Because three years ago I was stupid enough to think what I felt was love. OK, I'm angry about it, but that can be changed if you just admit your true nature.' He looked back at her, arching black brows. 'Tell me honestly that I'm right, that you did use me to further your career, and that you're now using Simon Mordant—and I'll give you the part.'

'You seriously expect me to lie to you like that?' she demanded bitterly. 'To pretend I'm a callous, heartless little——'

'It's what you are,' he cut in harshly. 'And if you admit to it, we can find a way to call an armed truce. Then you'll get the role you want, and I'll get the actress I want. Fair's fair, Chris. It's not——'

'Don't you dare call me Chris!' she said hoarsely, sipping her wine, her face flushed with angry emotion. 'Don't you ever call me Chris again.'

He looked startled. 'What...?'

'You heard me. I won't let you call me Chris. I can't stand to hear that nickname on your lips.'

'Why?' His smile grew barbed. 'Don't tell me it brings back fond memories, because you and I both know the truth about that!'

'The truth?' She gave an angry laugh, putting her glass down. 'You wouldn't know the truth if it came up and bit you!'

'Keep your voice down!'

'No, I will not, you vicious swine! I've had just about enough of this!' She pushed her chair back suddenly, making everyone in the room stare at her.

Jared's hand clamped over her wrist as he stared up at her, almost breathless with a combination of shock and rage. 'What the hell are you doing? Sit down!'

'I don't have to sit here and listen to this!' she said softly, keeping her voice low, smiling at him as she spoke. 'Not for Lelie, not for best actress, and certainly not for you!'

'If this is some kind of game——'

'It's not a game! It's the truth! I thought that was what you wanted? Shall I say it louder so everyone can hear?'

'No, damn it, and if you don't sit down right away you'll be out of the casting list for good!'

'Now there's a threat!' she whispered, feeling that inner conflict rise up and fight, her ambition struggling against her emotional needs. That golden, glittering dream was being overshadowed and instead of thinking, I have to have that role, all Christie could think was, he doesn't love me, he never loved me, he never really loved me...

She felt as though the world had gone crazy, and she was left in a topsy-turvy city where houses and buildings and trees were sliding all over an ever-shifting landscape where ambition simply could not do anything, ambition was suddenly a gun with a flower in it instead of a bullet.

'Anything wrong?' Millie cooed from the head of the table.

'Just a little disagreement,' Christie said, lifting her head, not giving a damn what Millie or anyone else thought of her. 'Mr Buchanan and I have such very different interpretations of Lelie's character.'

Jared gave a dry laugh. 'And Miss McCall is such a fiery actress! All temperament and no *prima donna*—the perfect choice for the role!'

'Definitely!' Mike Camarra drawled, watching them with narrowed eyes from his vantage point beside them, no doubt privy to a great deal of what they had said. 'And I'm glad you brought the subject up so soon, Christie. It needs a great deal of discussion before we start auditions. You've read the script?'

'Of course,' she murmured shakily, sitting down again and giving Mike a radiant smile. However emotional she got with Jared, Mike Camarra was still her boss, this was still her career, and she was not going to throw it all away, even if she had to eventually drop her ambitions to play Lelie. 'It's an excellent script, and I'm very, very interested in playing it. Thank you for offering it to me.'

Jared laughed beside her, drawling under his breath, 'Good volte-face, Chris! And I thought for a second you might be genuine!'

Angrily, she flushed, but did not turn her attention back to him.

'I see you in the first scene,' Mike Camarra was saying, smoking a cigar as the soup was cleared away, 'walking barefoot on a beach, wearing nothing but a tight, shabby red dress.'

'Shabby,' Jared murmured, eyes mocking Christie.

She tried to ignore him, but what she wanted to do was throw her soup over him. Luckily, the waiters began clearing the soup away at that moment, saving him from a face full of excellent clam chowder.

'And an overdub,' Mike continued, 'of your thoughts.'

'Ah, yes,' Jared drawled, 'what are her first lines in that scene? You've read the script, Christie. Why not perform for us now?'

Looking angrily at him, she lifted her head and quoted direct from the script, '"I must be famous, I must get there, no matter what it takes, who I have to trample on, use, abuse, hurt or destroy..."'

His hard, handsome face surveyed her with hatred. But she saw a glimmer of pain in his jet-black eyes that wrenched at her heart, made her want to suddenly fling herself into his arms, whispering that it wasn't true, she wasn't like that, had always loved him, still loved him, always would love him. Talk about a volte-face, she thought bitterly. Am I going mad, or am I just a fool?

'What are your thoughts on location, Jared?' Mike asked.

'Well, I've taken a look at the list of locations,' Jared replied, 'and the research footage of each, and I rather favour Mustique at the moment...'

They continued to discuss the film for the rest of the meal.

'Yes, I agree,' Mike was saying as they ate poussin with grapes, 'Lelie is a manipulative little whore. Intensely sexy, though. Every man in every cinema in every town all over the world will want to take her to bed.'

'Great box-office,' agreed Jared, his eyes glittering at Christie.

She ignored him studiously, but inside she was still a raging maelstrom of conflict.

Across the table, she saw that Simon and Nessa were having a similarly tempestuous evening. Concern rippled through her for poor Simon. He looked absolutely furious, his normally calm grey eyes blazing with passionate emotion. Nessa Vale looked like Countess Dracula, leaning back in her chair, a vituperative smile on her red lips as she delivered some insult to Simon which made him suddenly grip her by the wrist, leaning close to her, biting out a fierce reply under his breath. She had never seen him like this before. It was quite a revelation to see that elegant façade crack clean across to reveal a passionate lover. It suddenly dawned on her that there was far more to his relationship with Nessa Vale than had at first met the eye. She also remembered how evasive he had been when she'd asked how long his involvement with Nessa had lasted. Was it possible that Simon had been lying to her about his past life? And if so, why? He was clearly very deeply involved with Nessa. This was no faintly smouldering ember of an old flame: this was raging like a forest fire, and she was suddenly prepared to bet that Simon was very heavily in love with Nessa Vale.

'So you definitely want the role?' Mike's voice drew her back into the conversation.

'Yes, I...' She looked up as the coffee was served.

'Of course she wants it,' Jared declared beside her, admiring contempt in his dark eyes. 'She's perfect for it, and we all know it.'

'Yes, I'm beginning to think I am perfect for it!' Christie turned to look at him with a tight smile. 'Lelie may be amoral, but at least she doesn't subjugate herself to the men who want to manipulate *her*!'

There was a tense little silence.

That remark was for Jared, and he received it with a cool smile, eyes narrowing as he seemed to study her even more intently.

'Or hadn't that role reversal,' Christie said under her breath, 'occurred to you before, in your great scheme for revenge?'

He leaned close, murmuring tightly, 'Keep your voice down, behave yourself, and don't bring anyone else into our private war. Or I'll make you wish you'd never heard my name.'

'Too late,' she retorted under her breath. 'I reached that point about an hour ago!'

Their eyes warred angrily.

'Anything wrong?' Mike asked suddenly, watching them.

Jared lifted his dark head. 'Nothing at all,' he returned coolly, getting to his feet with a smile. 'Just that Miss McCall and I were planning to discuss the film in greater depth tonight, and we've decided to combine our conversation with a breath of fresh air. All this wine . . . I think a walk on the beach—don't you, Miss McCall?'

Cornered, Christie had no real option other than to smile sweetly and say, 'What a lovely idea!' Getting to her feet, she met Simon's startled gaze as he looked up. 'Don't worry, darling. We're just going to talk about *Tigresse*. Besides, you know I'm yours, and I can assure you Mr Buchanan is most definitely not my type!'

'That's not what I've heard,' said Nessa Vale.

Christie gave her a filthy look, and left the dining-room with Jared. Outside, the marble hall was cool, their footsteps echoed on its black and white surface, and far above the chandeliers swayed gently.

'And you accuse me of being manipulative,' Christie said, walking beside him, gold high heels click-clacking as her ivory silk dress rippled loosely on her slender body. 'That was very neatly done—getting me out here for a private conversation while pretending it was for the sake of the film!'

'It is for the sake of the film.' He strode with his usual dynamism. 'Regardless of our personal differences, we will have to work together on *Tigresse*, and we'll have to find a way to bury the hatchet.'

'I shall refrain from the obvious reply!'

He laughed, wrenched open the great double doors, and the full moon glowed like a spotlight at a première in that deep blue, star-studded sky as they walked out into the grounds. The night was balmy-sweet, crickets chirping in the shrubbery surrounding the house which the sea swooshed gently against the sands.

'And maybe I don't want that part, anyway,' Christie said tightly under her breath as they walked. 'Maybe it's not worth the trouble.'

'Yes, so you claimed at dinner.' He idly tore a leaf from a shrub. 'I almost believed you, too. That sincerity in your voice, the hurt look in your eyes . . . where *did* you learn the technique?'

'From you!' she said thickly, hating him. 'When you told me you loved me and wanted to spend the rest of your life with me!'

'I was genuine and you know it,' he said roughly.

'Well, your idea of love obviously conflicts with mine, Jared, because, as far as I'm concerned you can't turn it on and off like a camera or a wind machine!'

'You have to, if you want to keep your sanity.' His voice thickened, and as she glanced sideways at him she saw the dark glitter of angry emotion in his eyes.

Was it possible that he still felt something for her? But no—how could it be! He had been such a swine to her since he arrived here. He obviously thought her the lowest form of female life, just because she had wanted to be a success.

'So when did you decide to keep your sanity and throw away love?' she asked tightly. 'Or shall I guess? Was it perhaps the moment you realised I was serious about becoming a famous actress?'

'Do you really care, Chris?' They arrived at the gates to the private beach. 'I mean—does it make any difference to know the exact moment when love turned to hate?'

'Of course it makes a difference!' she said fiercely. 'If I knew when you started to feel this contempt and hatred for me, it would help me deal with my own feelings for you!'

'Feelings?' he bit out thickly. 'You don't have any feelings!' He pushed open the gates with an angry shove and strode through on to the little path that led to the sands.

'Oh, that's right!' she followed him, furious and hurt. 'I don't have any feelings, do I! I'm supposed to be able to sit back and take your insults, your contempt and your power-hungry manipulations without——'

'You'll do it if you want that part!'

'Well, maybe I don't want it enough to put up with the way you're treating me!' she cried passionately.

He stopped, turning, catching the pain in her voice. For a split-second he studied her, the warm breeze lifting his black hair from his tanned forehead as the sea glittered in the moonlight behind him.

'No,' he bit out under his breath, and started walking away down the beach again. 'I won't fall for it, Chris. Not again. Not ever again. Now, I want to hear the truth for once. Just tell me exactly how you played the game with me three years ago. All of it. I can take it. I no longer love you. I just want to——'

He stopped in the silence, suddenly realising she had not moved.

Turning to stare at her, he was silent, too, unaware that she was blind with tears, pain welling up inside her like a tidal wave. The conflict was reaching a climax inside her, and she knew what was going to happen; she was going to snap, break, tell him she didn't want the role, and really mean it, but she couldn't believe she'd do that, couldn't believe she'd throw away that golden prize just because he was hurting her, but it was coming, the moment was almost there.

'What's the matter?' Jared asked her tersely, moving to stand a few feet away. 'Why are you just waiting there like a statue?'

'My shoes,' she said thickly, lifting her chin, her mouth trembling. 'I can't walk across the sand in high heels.'

'Take them off. Then you really will be just like Lelie. A barefoot whore on the beach thinking of nothing but fame and fortune!' He laughed, jeering, 'I can't decide whether or not to demand sexual favours from you as well as a full confession! I'm willing to bet you'd turn cartwheels in my bed just to get that part! You did it for me three and a half years ago, didn't you, when you thought I might put you in one of my pictures? It must have been a shock to realise you'd been wasting your sexual skills on me! No wonder you turned to Simon. He really paid up, didn't he? How many new skills have you learned with him? Maybe I——'

'Shut up!' Christie tore her shoes off and threw them at his head, one after the other. 'Shut up, shut up, shut up!'

'Hey!' He jerked back but the first shoe hit him hard on the side of his head. 'Ow!' The second shoe hit him on the eyebrow. 'Stop it!'

'No, you stop it!' she shouted hoarsely. 'Stop hurting me, talking to me like this, calling me all sorts of unspeakable names!'

'I'm your director and ex-lover! I can speak to you any way I like!'

'Not any more, you can't!' She was on the verge of breaking down completely, her voice shaking. 'I'm not putting up with another second of this—let alone a whole filming schedule under your vicious command! So you can just stick your lead role where the sun doesn't shine, because I'd die rather than play Lelie now! Do you hear me? I'd rather *die*!' Turning, she walked back to the gate in bare feet, her heart banging so loud she thought it might leap out of her body and land on the sandy path.

Jared raced after her, caught her arm, and spun her to face him. 'I know what you're doing! Trying to make me feel guilty so I'll give you the part and stop treating you as you deserve to be——'

'Don't you understand English? I don't want the part!'

'Liar!' His eyes blazed black rage. 'You'd do anything to get it!'

'Watch my lips! I do not want the part. I do not want the——'

'If this is some trick to make me——'

'It's not a trick! It's the final straw! I wanted to play Lelie, but if this is a taste of the medicine you're going to give me, you can get stuffed, because I'm *not* going to swallow it down like a good girl!'

'You wouldn't know how! You're a bad girl from way back!'

'Jared, I don't want the part!' she shouted, shaking with emotion.

'I don't believe you!'

'Perhaps you will when you wake up tomorrow to find I've left Casa Camarra!'

There was a stunned silence. He breathed harshly, staring down into her angry face, seeing the fierce glare of her eyes, the sheen of helpless tears shimmering on them, and the way her whole body trembled with emotion from head to foot.

'Don't be absurd,' he bit out under his breath. 'You can't leave without Millie's say-so, and we both know she's never going to give it.'

'I don't care!' she said hoarsely, tears threatening to spill.

'Come on! Of course you care! You're going for the biggest prize on the list, aren't you?' His upper lip curled back in a sneer. 'Christie McCall, up there in the heavens with Harlow, Garbo, Monroe and Vivien Leigh! A Hollywood superstar!'

'Why shouldn't I want to be a star?' She snapped, lost control, completely lost it, and flew at him, hands slapping and punching his chest as she cried, 'Why shouldn't I want to be famous? Why not? It's all that keeps me alive, all that gets me from day to day, and it always has been, ever since I was a little girl, it's the only thing I have to live for, the only thing I *ever* had to live for!' The tears spilled over her lashes. 'And don't tell me other people live for love—I never had love to live for! Nobody ever loved me! You know they didn't, you know about my family, you know I had no love from—— '

'I loved you!' he bit out thickly.

'No, you didn't, Jared!' she flung back fiercely. 'You only loved what you wanted me to be! A woman who would support your career, give you children, and worship nightly at the shrine of the great Jared Buchanan!'

His face ran with angry colour. 'That's a lie! I didn't need you to support my career—I was already a big success when we met, and my career was established. I had a career, Christie, long before we even spoke of marriage!'

'So did I, Jared!'

'Yes, but it wasn't anywhere near as successful as mine!'

'That's just about what I'd expect from you!' she spat in tearful despair, breaking away from him, eyes blazing. 'It's all right for *you* to want your name in lights, it's all right for you to need fame and——'

'You know damned well why I wanted to be powerful!' he shouted angrily. 'I was an orphan, jumbled up in a children's home, lost in the shuffle, overlooked at all times! If I wanted money and prestige, it was hardly a selfish drive to have!'

'Oh, yes, it's all right for you to have had a rotten life, to have spent your whole childhood dreaming of being famous, of stamping your name so firmly into film history that everybody cowers the minute they hear that great, hallowed name—Jared Buchanan!'

'Shut up!'

She curtsied mockingly. 'Yes, Sir Jared!'

He made a grab at her.

She danced out of his way, laughing. 'Pardon me, *Mr* Buchanan, for having the sheer nerve to want to be famous myself!'

'Don't try to fling that at me! It isn't like that and it never was!'

'Then what was it like!' she demanded, eyes blazing. 'Come on—you tell me! What was it you said way back when? Oh, yes—now I remember! That I wasn't talented enough to be as high-and-mighty famous as you!'

'I didn't say it like that!'

'And what has your behaviour been in aid of since we got here? Why all the threats and power-plays, if not to have me eating enough humble pie to feed Lassie for a lifetime!'

'I just want to know the truth, damn you!' he said
gruffly, and she saw his mouth shake a second before
he turned away, running a hand through his thick black
hair, staring fixedly at the sand, a glimmering sheen
across his dark eyes. He drew a harsh breath, biting his
knuckles for a second, before he said raggedly, 'I just
want to know the truth. That's all there is to it. I admit,
I've been cruel, and that I—I would like to see you eating
humble pie. But what I really want is the truth.'

'The truth?' she asked huskily. 'The truth is that I was
in love with you, and thought you loved me. I did tell
you, back then, that I wanted to be famous. You can't
say I didn't. It was all we talked about that first week
we met. Don't say you don't remember that, Jared. Don't
say you've——' she drew an unsteady breath, her voice
cracking '—forgotten that.'

'No.' His voice was as racked with as much emotion
as hers as they stood there, two tormented lovers on the
deserted, moonlit beach. 'No, I remember that first week
as clearly as if it were yesterday.'

'Thank God for small mercies!' she said hoarsely, and
sank down on to the sand, putting her face in her hands,
the tears suddenly spilling out over her cheeks. 'At least
you can remember me with *some* affection!'

He sighed harshly, watched her cry alone for a second,
then sank down beside her on the sand. The sea washed
in and out in the darkness. The moonlight glowed over
her slender body as she cried, the dam breaking now,
and flooding her with all the emptiness that had been
building in her for weeks, revealing the extent of her
loneliness to her for the first time.

'Why are you crying like this?' he asked in the end,
sounding cool, although his voice was unsteady.

'Because nobody loves me! Nobody ever has!' she
whispered through her tears. 'I've got no one, I never

have had, and I can't bear to face it, even now, when I've got all the fame I want...'

'Ah...!' He handed her the handkerchief from his top jacket pocket, putting his arm around her, tenderness suddenly shining in his dark eyes as he said, 'Nobody loves you, everybody hates you, you're going in the garden to eat worms.'

'Don't laugh at me, Jared!' she whispered brokenly.

'You sound so sweet,' he said deeply, staring at her. 'Like a little girl!'

'I am a little girl!' she said and blew her nose. 'Just as you're a little boy.'

'*Vive la différence* ...!' he murmured, long fingers playing with the silk of her dress in the cool sands.

'And that's what this comes down to, Jared. You think I should be perpetually dressed in pink, playing mummies and daddies in my doll's house—while you run around in the big jungle of life, climbing trees and fighting battles!'

He laughed softly, looking up, eyes loving. 'Chris— you're not trying to tell me, after all this time, that you're a tomboy?'

'I just like adventure and excitement and achievement,' she said huskily. 'If that makes me a tomboy—then that's what I must be.'

'Not you.' His hand touched her long sensual blonde hair, and his voice roughened. 'I've never known a more feminine woman in my life.'

Her eyes met his, her face dry of tears now, and she felt her heart turn over with the love she saw in his eyes.

'Chris...' he said unsteadily, and then he was drawing her towards him, lowering his dark head, leaving her time to pull away, but she didn't, couldn't, too bewitched by the mutual spell of love that made her hands move to his broad shoulders, her lips part, her head tilt back and her eyes close. They kissed sweetly, tenderly, his hands sliding to frame her face. He gently kissed the last tears away, then his mouth sought hers again, opening it with growing passion, seemingly hesitant, and then incredulous that she returned his excitement with a passionate, abandoned kiss of her own, her arms locking around his strong neck.

His breath caught, then the kiss flared into terrible hunger as he gave a rough exclamation, pushing her back on the sands, his powerful body covering hers, his mouth moving with deep need on hers, tongues meeting and hot breathing mingling fiercely.

'Oh, God, Chris...!' he said hoarsely against her bruised, swollen lips, and she moaned in answering desire, her mouth open beneath his, kissing him back hungrily, desperately, gasping at the feel of his skin, his tongue, the taste and scent of him, so wonderful, like water to a woman dying of thirst as her fingers moved through his thick, glossy hair, touched his skin, his skin, his skin...

Drowning in sensation, dizzy with it, she knew she shouldn't let this kiss continue because of all the terrible things he'd said, but how could she think, how could she even attempt to, when her body was flooding with overwhelming feelings, and she was at last allowed to express her pent-up love, desire and loneliness—with the man she loved.

Suddenly, his hand was stroking her breast and she arched towards him, saying yes, yes, yes... He gave a rough groan, fingers tugging down the silky bodice of her dress, exposing her to the warm Californian sea air, his hand gripping her bare breast. He thrust one hard thigh between hers, a strangled cry in his throat as he bent his head, breathing harshly, to close that hot mouth over her erect pink nipple.

'Chris,' he whispered, 'let me make love to you...'

'I can't, Jared!' She was shivering with love and desire. 'But—oh, darling, when you call me Chris, it's like being back there, in that flat, just the two of us, so much in love...'

'Chris...!' He raised his head, breathing hard, and there was sudden agony in his eyes as he said hoarsely, 'What happened to us?'

CHAPTER FIVE

THEY stared at each other in the moonlit darkness, the only sounds those of their heartbeats, their unsteady breathing, and the sea washing slowly in and out on the sands. Suddenly, Christie realised they had turned some massive secret corner in their relationship, as though for these few precious moments on the beach they were being honest with each other, just as open and loving and trusting as they had been three and a half years ago. Hostility was suspended now that they had argued, fought, cried, and then begun to make love to each other. The physical contact had broken down the barriers, and even though she knew they could just as quickly rise up again to separate them, she was prepared to leap into these deep waters of love with him, and trust him not to let her drown.

'You gave me that ultimatum, Jared,' Christie said huskily. 'You said to me, "If you go to Los Angeles ... we're finished."'

'And you replied, "All right, then—we're finished!"'

'Well, what else could I say?' she demanded, blue eyes filling with pain at the memory. 'You made it clear with that ultimatum that you wanted to stand in the way of my dreams.'

His eyes darkened. 'I thought one of your dreams was to marry me, Chris! That's what you kept telling me back then, isn't it? My God, you used to lie awake in my arms thinking up names for the children we were supposedly going to have!'

'I didn't just lie awake thinking of names of our children,' she said huskily. 'I told you I wanted to wait before we had them—remember?'

'I thought you meant a few months, maybe a year——'

'No, I was thinking more in terms of five years. Having children when I was thirty, and had made my career.'

'So easy to say now, Chris! But you didn't say it back then! You lied to me, let me think you loved me, let me believe you wanted the same things I wanted—and then left me!' His voice shook with sudden fierce emotion. 'And you wonder why I feel bitter about the way you treated me!'

'Jared, I loved you!' Her voice was husky, urgent, her hands suddenly gripping his broad shoulders, trying to dispel the bitterness in his eyes and bring back the love, the trust, the honesty. 'I thought I'd found everything I ever wanted with a man. You know I was a virgin when we met. I'd never been as deeply involved with anyone as I became with you, right from the start. And I was twenty-five, Jared. It must have been blatantly obvious that I wanted to marry you, have your children.'

'But here we are,' he said thickly, 'three years later, and you're going to marry Simon Mordant—the man you left me for!'

'I didn't leave you for him! I left you for my dreams! I had other dreams apart from being your wife and having your children—why is that so difficult to accept?'

'Because you're still with Simon!' he bit out harshly. 'Why is *that* so difficult to accept? You knew I was jealous of him, even then!'

'I only met him in March,' she reminded him. 'I only knew him for three months before I came out here to Hollywood.'

'And for that time you were always with him! When I came home at night, his name was practically the first thing you mentioned! I knew I was losing you to Simon Mordant—long before you left!'

She nodded, eyes pained. 'I know it must have seemed that way. But there was never anything between me and Simon. Please try to believe that, Jared. We weren't lovers then—and we're not lovers now, even if we are engaged to be——'

'Oh, please!' He gave a rough laugh, his mouth tightening as he looked down at her with angry dark eyes. 'You don't seriously expect me to believe that, do you? That you've been together for three years, a relationship that's culminating in marriage, and you've never been to bed together? What kind of fool do you think I am!'

'I know it seems unlikely, but then it was very unlikely for you to meet a twenty-five-year-old actress who was a virgin.' Her blue eyes studied him with love, a smile curving her full mouth as she added huskily, 'I remember you said so at the time...'

He just stared at her, breathing hard, and she knew her words had at least got through to him, if not made him completely believe her. It occurred to her that she was asking a lot of him to believe that she and Simon weren't lovers. But what else could she do? It was the truth, and she had vowed to tell him the truth in these precious moments alone, regardless of the outcome or whether or not he believed her. All that mattered to her was the deep intimacy they had suddenly rediscovered. It was the first real taste of love she had had since she left him.

'All right,' he said unsteadily after a moment. 'I concede the unlikeliness of meeting a twenty-five-year-old virgin actress. But once I'd unleashed your sexuality, Chris, it blazed as high and fierce as mine. You took to making love like a dream come true. I can understand that you were happy to be celibate beforehand. But after you'd tasted the forbidden apple?'

His mouth tightened. 'No. You can't possibly have lived the last three years without a lover. I simply don't believe it.'

Christie gave a deep sigh. 'Well, what can I say, Jared...?'

'Nothing.' His voice was rough with emotion, dark eyes filled with pain, regret. 'God knows why I'm even listening to you at all. I should have my head examined. Any woman who can lie here and tell me she's not sexually involved with her own fiancé *must* think I'm a fool.' His hand touched her cheek as he whispered thickly, 'Trouble is, I want so badly to believe you that I'm prepared to risk it. And maybe I also know that there's a way to prove what you're saying.'

Her eyes darted up to his, a look of enquiry in them. 'How...?'

'How do you think?' His heart started to thud hard in his chest, his body pressing against hers now, the fierce thrust of his manhood suddenly burning against her thigh again. 'Chris, if you're lying, your body will betray you. And if you're telling the truth...' He bent his dark head, his hot mouth burning a trail against her shivering throat. 'Oh, God, you'll feel like a virgin to me again.'

She caught her breath with a rush of excitement as his hard mouth closed over hers. The kiss was intense, passionate, sweeping them both into immediate arousal as their mouths clung, their bodies moving in a rocking, abandoned rhythm, and all she could do was lie back accepting it blindly, her love for him combining with a sudden realisation that she had been denying her body its own fierce needs for too long.

His strong hands were fondling her breasts again, long fingers stroking the nipples, sending hot needles of fierce sexual desire through her as she moaned beneath that hot, demanding mouth and arched her body into his hands willingly. He bent his head. His face was flushed with excitement. His mouth closed over her breast, sucked hungrily at the nipple, and sent her into delirious excitement.

'Has it really been three years for you, Chris?' he asked hoarsely, still sucking at her nipple while one strong hand moved slowly to ruck her silk evening gown up to the thigh.

'Yes, yes...!' She was spiralling with desire, blind and dizzy now, the memories flooding back, unbending her body as though it had been locked up, covered in dust, forgotten and imprisoned for three years, its only function to be exercised ruthlessly then paraded on film in perfect clothes. But this was what it was built for.

His hands were stroking her rear now, his rough groans of excitement making her bold, gasping against his hot mouth, slowly sucking his tongue which always drove him wild in its direct symbolism, while her fingers began to shakingly undo the white evening shirt he wore.

'Ah, Chris...!' He was almost incoherent with desire. 'You're even sexier now than you were back then...success has made a siren out of you!'

Her hands pushed his shirt apart and she ran her fingers over his hard, hair-roughened chest, remembering it so well, the sheen of his tanned skin bringing back hot memories of his nude body, the hard-muscled power of it, and how uninhibited she had been with him then, never afraid to be naked with him, or to express herself in the most sexual sense.

He kissed her again, his mouth sensually provocative on hers, and she felt his strong hands slide slowly between her legs, gently rubbing the hot nub of flesh through her silky briefs, then sliding inside, making her give a low, long moan of guttural excitement as his fingers stroked the hot slippery flesh itself.

'Oh, darling...!' he bit out hoarsely, barely able to breathe as he touched her. 'Oh God, you're so ex-

cited . . . let me make love to you, please, my darling, I
think I'm going to explode at any minute . . . !'

'We've let it go too far!' she whispered with a fierce
sob of frustration and despair, knowing it was impossible to let this happen, to let it reach its passionate
conclusion. 'You know I can't let you take me, not like
this, not without real love, not while——'

'You can't stop me now, you mustn't . . .' he said shakingly, and his finger slid inside her, making her moan
with acute excitement, her legs sliding further apart for
him, making him cry out suddenly, his heart hammering
like a drum gone mad as he took his hand from her,
dragging air into his lungs, his hands going to the belt
of his trousers. 'Oh, Chris, Chris . . . it's been so long!'

'No!' She came to her senses, staring in horror as he
fumbled to undo his trousers. 'Jared, don't force me,
don't even think about it! I said no and I meant it!'

There was a long, fraught silence. He stared down at
her with dazed eyes, his face flushed deep red and his
breathing so ragged she thought he'd never catch his
breath again. His heart was hammering violently at his
chest.

'Apart from the fact that we've only just met up again
after three years,' Christie said shakingly, 'there's also
the fact that Simon is still my fiancé! We may not be
lovers, but I owe him fidelity and I could never live with
myself if I betrayed him, out here, with you.'

'You don't feel you've betrayed him already?' he asked
thickly.

'I . . .' Hot colour burned her cheeks, and guilt ran
through her like wildfire, but she was only human, she
loved Jared, and what had happened had been an accident, not a deliberate rendezvous.

'Oh, but maybe you're so used to betraying men,
it doesn't make any difference!' he said in a voice
that shook.

Stung, she whispered fiercely, 'No, I don't feel I've betrayed him. If I've betrayed anyone tonight it's been myself. I should never have let this get so far—both emotionally and sexually.'

His eyes closed, and he said roughly, 'Then why did you, Chris?'

'How can you even ask that? You must have seen how swept away I was! Not just by your lovemaking, but by everything you said—even before you kissed me, I was almost yours for the taking.'

His body was still rigid with excitement; she could feel his manhood pulsing violently against her inner thigh. 'But you're not mine for the taking now,' he observed, arching dark brows. 'And don't throw Simon bloody Mordant at me as an excuse. I know you're engaged to him, and therefore the proprieties should be observed. But if what you say is true about your relationship with him—and I'm prepared at this moment to believe it is— then your refusal to make love with me now is nothing whatever to do with that part of your life.'

She flushed angrily, guilt increasing in her, because of course he was right, and she didn't like knowing how easily her feelings for Jared could completely sweep Simon out of the way.

'Is it?'

Her cheeks burnt hotter. 'No!' She lifted blazing eyes to his. 'It's to do with the past, Jared, and the fact that I don't feel we've sorted our relationship out nearly enough to be able to make love.'

'Ah...' His lashes flickered as though he was surprised by what she said, but his hard mouth curved in a smile too, and she knew he had suspected what her answer would be. 'So we still have a lot to thrash out between us before I can make love to you again?'

'I'm still engaged to Simon!' she said angrily. 'And I haven't said a word to you about agreeing to make love— serious conversation about the past or no!'

'The faithful fiancé!' he drawled mockingly.

Rage leapt in her eyes. 'Right, that does it!' She tried to sit up, furious with herself for having trusted him at all.

'Hey!' He sat up too, holding her, his eyes intense. 'I'm sorry! I was just making a jealous little snipe at you, that's all. Don't get all defensive again and storm away from me!'

Her eyes met his, and she suddenly put her hands on his broad shoulders, that white shirt open to reveal the power of his tanned and muscular chest, making her feel weak with love and longing. 'Jared, it's just that I'm so scared of even beginning this conversation!'

'*You're* scared!' He laughed thickly, his smile sardonic.

'We have to be so brutally honest with each other. Look what happened last time, when we skirted around the truth and swept all our real desires under the carpet every time we sensed disapproval from the other...'

He watched her, his eyes dark, and his body tense.

'That's why it ended in that ultimatum,' she said huskily. 'Because we'd both been so busy trying to avoid little arguments that in the end a massive row was inevitable.'

He gave a harsh sigh, looking away. 'You're right. I guess it was because we were only together for six months. And most of that time I was so wrapped up at the studio. We just didn't have time to be brutally honest. So we tried to keep the whole thing together as best we could.'

'And hid what we really thought,' she reminded him huskily. 'I always told you I was ambitious. I talked often about my career, my dreams, my goals. But every time

I saw the disapproval in your eyes I'd clam up, and start talking about marriage and children again.'

'Oh, no...!' He winced, putting a hand to his forehead, eyes closing. 'No... I can't bear to think that you didn't mean a word of——'

'Now, don't go making the same mistakes again!' she said fiercely, her hands gripping his shoulders. 'I *did* mean it. All of it. Every last imagined little son with your eyes and hair.'

A flush touched his face as he smiled, and he darted a brief, shining look at her. 'You wanted to call them all Jared the Second, the Third, the Fourth...'

She laughed softly, kissing him. 'Yes, I did. I really did. But I didn't just want that, Jared.'

'You wanted your career, too,' he said thickly, nodding. 'I realised that gradually over the last three years. Bit of a horror story, really, for me. Having to stand back and watch you climb higher, higher, right up to the Oscars ceremony. I was afraid to think about what I'd done, how I'd tried to stand in your way, so I just hated you instead...somehow it was easier. I can't think why I did it. It only hurt me. Twisted me up inside, made me even more cynical than I was when I met you. Fear, I suppose. It's a brave man who can face the truth about himself.'

'You were also afraid to truly love me,' she said huskily. 'You always wanted me to be the perfect woman, didn't you, Jared? Some ideal of the 1950s, dusting the happy home in her pinny, devoting herself to children and husband, never a thought or dream or ambition of her own entering her pretty little head...'

'That was my vision of family life,' he said sharply, frowning at her. 'OK, so it wasn't realistic. But it was something of a survival mechanism for me in my childhood. Besides—how else was I supposed to see family life? All I had were the other lost boys and the

House Mother. Apart from that, there were films—and all the films I liked best had happy families in them.'

Christie put her arms around him and kissed his strong neck. 'Darling, I didn't mean to sound as though I——'

'No, of course not.' His hands took her wrists, pulled her away from him, surveying her face with hard, angry eyes. 'A pity you did.'

There was a brief silence.

'And I'm sure,' she said in a tight, hurt voice, 'that you didn't mean to make me feel guilty for not being able to fulfil that ideal role of womanhood for you.'

Rage leapt in his eyes. 'I was not trying to make you feel guilty! I just didn't like the way you talked about being a wife and mother. It isn't a job to sneer at, Chris! You can't just do it for eight or nine months the way you can a film role!

'You hardly need to remind me,' she said, brows arching. 'I remember only too well how hard I slaved trying to *be* that perfect housewife for you, and all I got were complaints and endless criticism.'

He arched his brows too. 'Well, the beds were always unmade, the cupboards empty and——'

'Here we go again!'

'Chris,' he snapped, 'you agreed to move in with me and give it a go!'

'For your sake, not for mine!'

'As I found out to my cost! What you wanted was the pay-cheque, the glory and the glamour—not an ordinary, loving home!'

'I did want a loving home, Jared, I just——'

'God, you bloody liar!' he bit out forcefully. 'How you can sit there and tell me that, I'll never know! You've made it clear at every step of the last three years that *all* you're interested in having is money and fame!'

'Yes, and that's the real problem between us, isn't it, Jared?' she shouted back fiercely. 'You didn't just make that ultimatum because of Simon's presence in my life. You made it because you did *not* want me to be a success. You wanted to cut me in half and make me be nothing more or less than the perfect wife, while *you* went on gathering all the international film trophies!'

'That's a filthy lie and you know it!' he ground out between his teeth, as he always did when he wanted to dissuade her from pointing out a fundamental truth.

'Oh?' She studied his strong, handsome face. 'Are you sure about that, Jared? Let's try to put all the pieces together, shall we?'

He shifted angrily, his face hard. 'What pieces? What are you talking about?'

'The pieces of the Jared Buchanan jigsaw puzzle.' Her eyes were completely without pretence or malice or emotion. She had never felt such urgency to tell the absolute truth in her life before—and at the same time such strong pressure to make sure it was not bungled by losing her temper or getting emotional or flying off the handle in passionate recrimination. For three years, she had put this jigsaw puzzle together in her head, needing badly to understand why it had all happened between them, just as it had, and she was now very well versed on every single piece that had gone to make up the man she loved—it was imperative she did not make a mess of her equation.

'Oh, I'm a jigsaw puzzle too, am I?' he drawled with a sardonic smile, and suddenly rolled to one side of her, resting his dark head on his hand, watching her in the moonlight, his eyes cynical as he tried to deflect attention from himself by turning the spotlight on her. 'How interesting that we should both reach the same conclusion about each other. You're not the only one who's spent the last three years counting up pieces, you know. How do you think I realised you were just like Lelie?'

Her lashes flickered. Anger coursed through her veins at his deliberate attack. She kept herself under control and said coolly, 'My turn first, I think, Jared. After all, you've already had a good run for your money tonight. Insults flying right, left and centre. Surely I should have a chance to even the score?'

He studied her darkly, then laughed, looked away and said huskily, 'Go ahead. What have I got to lose?'

'Your illusions?' she suggested softly.

He turned back, burningly angry. 'I am a thirty-eight-year-old man, at the top of my profession, with a chequered past of major experience with women! I cannot possibly be accused of still harbouring any illusions!'

'Oh, I don't know about that,' she said carefully, watching him. 'After all, the last thing on your list of achievements was marriage, wasn't it, Jared? I remember your telling me that when we first met.'

'How very trusting I must have been,' he said, eyes narrowed.

'You said you had always known you wouldn't marry until your career was completely secure,' she reminded him. 'And that you'd always dreamed of a traditional marriage.'

His eyes flashed. 'What's wrong with a traditional marriage? Lots of people still make them. The wife stays at home, doesn't work, looks after the children, the house, the husband and——'

'And is unlikely to be an ambitious young woman with dreams of reaching international stardom as an actress, Jared!' Her mouth trembled faintly. 'I mean—why did you pick me in the first place? What on earth made you think I'd give it all up just to cook you roast dinners and darn your socks during my pregnancies?'

'Because you said you wanted to do it!' His eyes glimmered with rage. 'You said you wanted children, wanted——'

'I wanted it all!' she cried. 'Can't you understand that? All right! I'm a woman—I need to have children and I need to marry! But I'm a human being before I'm any of that, and I have dreams, ambitions, mountains to climb!'

'Pregnant women can't climb mountains!'

'Well, now you know why I don't want to have children yet!'

'You still don't want them?' He sounded appalled.

Pain lit her eyes as she heard herself confess, 'I'm watching the clock now. But not until I've climbed my mountains...'

'But you're twenty-eight now! You'll be too old to have children by the time you've run out of mountains to climb!'

'Not if I get the role of Lelie!' she said excitedly, without thinking. 'Jared, don't you see? It's the answer to all my problems! I'll be so famous by the time that's been out on general release for a year that I'll be able to retire for seven years or so, to have and bring up my children.'

Jared's face had hardened as she spoke, but so excited was she by her great plan for the future that she didn't spot it until she had finished speaking, and then she noticed it with a sinking heart, realising her mistake.

'I see,' Jared said tightly, a flash of rage in his eyes. 'And that's all planned out for you and Simon, is it?'

She went very still, suddenly aware of the depths of his rage.

'So where do I fit in? Or shall I guess?' His voice shook as he bit out, 'Sitting here on this bloody beach with you, being wound right round your manipulative little finger to make sure you *do* get that role!'

'Darling——' She reached for him in panic.

'Don't you touch me!' he whispered bitingly, slapping her hand away, and getting to his feet, so angry his eyes were like black knives as he towered above her, the moonlight behind him, silhouetting his powerful body against the glittering dark sea. 'And to think I nearly fell for it! I really believed you were my Chrissie-baby again, believed you loved me, and could still love——'

'But I did, I do, I——' She was scrambling to her feet too, eyes panic-stricken.

'You lying little bitch!' he said hoarsely, dark colour invading his face. 'How did you do it? How did it start? It must have been the tears—I thought they came out of the blue! And then the sweet, tender lovemaking followed by the refusal, and the loving confessions! Oh, what an Oscar-winner you are, my darling!'

'Don't think like this!' She flew at him in desperation, gripping his broad shoulders. 'Everything that's happened tonight will be destroyed if you don't keep believing in——'

'Oh, don't you worry about your precious little plans for the future, Christie McCall!' he bit out thickly. 'You'll get everything you want! The part, the fame, the power, the whole black bloody business! I'll eat my Cadillac convertible if you actually end up having children in a few years' time, but that's hardly my business right now, although I *do* believe you'll marry Simon Mordant!' His eyes filled with hatred. 'But right now I'm the one in the ultimate position of power over you, because only I can give you the role you crave so badly, and I can assure you I intend to demand something in return for it!'

'Jared...' she whispered, hands still on his shoulders as she stared up in horror at his angry face. 'Please stop this...please...'

'Don't you want to know what the price tag is, Chris?' he taunted softly, eyes glittering. 'Sure you do! Ambitious game-planner like you! You need to know every price along the way from every man you choose to tangle with in the name of your career!'

Christie felt tears biting into her eyes. 'Please don't do this... please...'

'Tears, sincerity, just the right touch of raw pain in the voice.' His eyes savaged her. 'Wonderful stuff. But this isn't an artistic audition, darling. I'm sure I don't have to say any more for you to guess just what kind of audition it's going to be.'

'Jared...' She was breathless with horror.

'On the casting couch,' he said bitingly. 'Midnight tomorrow. My bedroom.'

She drew a long, shaking breath. 'You don't seriously think I'd ever agree to that kind of proposition, do you?'

'You will if you want that picture.' His face was harshly implacable. 'But I'll give you twenty-four hours to make up your mind. I know you'll come to the only possible decision in the end. And I'll be waiting for you tomorrow night, with an exciting list of ways I want to make love to you in, a list I have no doubt will prove exquisitely——'

'Stop it!' she whispered thickly, trembling, her blue eyes blazing with anger and pain. 'How can you say such wicked things to me? Wicked...!'

'Wait till you see my list!' he drawled, running insolent, knowing, utterly unromantic eyes over her. 'That sexy little body of yours has long been number one on my midnight fantasy schedule. I can't wait to turn fantasy into reality, now that I know exactly who I was dealing with all along.'

'Jared, you're destroying everything!' she pleaded urgently with him, but if she had hoped to reach the loving, gentle, trusting man inside that hard protective shell, she was just asking to get hurt.

'It's already destroyed, Chris,' he said thickly. 'Just accept my terms or forget your dreams of glory.' He strode past her, his face hard, and she could only watch in numb despair as his powerful silhouette disappeared through the gates of the beach and into the gardens, while Casa Camarra rose in moonlit beauty far beyond…

CHAPTER SIX

So it had come to this. He was actually demanding that she go to bed with him in exchange for the role of Lelie. Christie had known Jared might go this far, but, of course, how could she have predicted it would be done with such hatred, savagery and vengeful anger? The very emotional conversation they had had just before he made his decision had no doubt triggered his towering determination to get back at her. And that was why she had been unable to stand up to him properly as he made his attack. She hadn't been rocketed out of her state of renewed love and trust; she had been fighting to keep it, to reach into his heart and drag him back to honesty, love, trust. Oh, if only she hadn't made that stupid confession of her deepest ambitions! She could see clearly now why he had reacted so violently. It must have sounded as though she would walk through fire to get the part of Lelie, and of course it was true: she would. The only fire she would balk at, though, was the fire of Jared's hatred and desire for sexual revenge. But given her past mistakes with Jared—and those wretched articles in the Hollywood Press—she could understand why he immediately assumed she was manipulating him into giving her the part with the minimum of fuss.

Were she anything like Lelie—this would be all in character. Lelie would certainly use Jared's seething emotions as a lever to get what she wanted. Lelie would definitely seduce him with lies, sweetness, tender confessions of love—just as Lelie would eventually concede defeat and go to the casting couch, prepared to give him the sexual experience of his life. Lelie would do *anything* to get that part.

But Christie was not Lelie. She had meant every word of her loveswept confessions, and she knew that Jared had, too. When you'd been in love with a man, and lived with him, you could tell when he was lying and when he wasn't. Jared still felt a great deal for her. But it was still so touch-and-go. Three years ago, they had split up for precisely the same reason: that when it came down to it, they had kept the truth hidden from each other— Jared by pretending he believed Christie's dreams would come true, and Christie herself for not having the courage to tell him directly what she really wanted from life. Consequently, they had each leapt to conclusions that were wrong, and gradually built up to an explosion of simmering resentment. That had happened again tonight when Jared leapt to the conclusion that she was using him to get the part so she could consolidate her position as an international superstar, and then retire to marry Simon.

She could hardly blame him. After all—she was engaged to Simon. And until this weekend had been more than prepared to marry him. In just a few short hours, Jared had changed all that by reminding her just exactly how it felt to be in love, truly in love, deeply in love. It wasn't just dark and destructive and dangerous. It was also wild, wonderful, filled with love, tenderness, humour, understanding and such exquisite passion.

God, she had forgotten how it felt to lie in his arms! The touch of his hands, the hot, commanding onslaught of his kiss as desire flared between them and they moved together as one . . . how could she even have half believed what she felt for Simon was love? It was nothing more than friendship, and although friendship could sometimes turn to love, it was love in friendship that never died. That was the difference. She and Jared were in love, and being friends was just a side effect of their love, but it was not the magnetic force that pulled them so powerfully together. How tempted she had been to make love with him. Only her fear of losing his love after finding it so recently had stopped her.

But she had wasted her breath, hadn't she? Because he had just smashed to pieces the shared intimacy they had rediscovered by returning to his rage, his belief that she was like Lelie, and making his demand that she go to bed with him in order to further her career.

Of course, she would not even consider the casting couch as a means to getting a part. Old Hollywood tradition it might be, but in reality it simply wasn't necessary, and only those with loose morals or very little self-respect were prepared to leap from bed to bed in search of stardom. Christie had never done it—nor would she start now.

That left her only one choice to make.

She would have to refuse the role altogether.

Tears stung her eyes as she stood there on the beach, her dreams scattering to the soft, warm breeze off the Pacific as the sea washed gently in and out, as though erasing her future in the sands.

Of course, there would be other roles, she told herself, bending to pick up her gold evening shoes. Not so brilliant, not such big box-office, but, nevertheless, other roles. Mike Camarra would be very angry with her, but, as he knew, she and Jared had always been a difficult proposition owing to their love affair in the past . . . how could he object too strongly? It wouldn't be worth his while to sue Christie or put her on a blacklist. Jared had obviously warned him that there might be trouble if Christie was cast in a Jared Buchanan picture. At any rate, whatever Mike's reaction, she would have to risk it. Anything to prevent Jared destroying her soul by forcing her on to the casting couch.

Walking back to the house, she felt the tears slipping over her lashes. So much for her great career plans! Jared had come along at the most critical point of her career and forced her to make the same choice he had forced her to make three years ago! How very typical of him, she thought with a hoarse laugh, dashing away her tears. And how very odd to find that, three years down the line, she was now going to make the other choice. Not career at any price. Not fame at any cost. But love, dignity and self-respect over and above all worldly ambitions.

The house was well-lit, a maid standing in the hall, while a number of guests were still up, roaring with laughter and chat in the drawing-room to the left, the door faintly ajar, the sound of music wafting softly from the hi-fi, and the loudest sound of all, Millie's high-pitched laughter.

Christie smiled politely at the maid and walked upstairs, barefoot on the rich red carpet, one hand on the polished banister, watched by Vivien Leigh, Valentino and Jean Harlow.

Suddenly, she heard a commotion on the east corridor.

'Get out, you rotten swine!'

'Nessa, listen to me, for God's sake!'

'No!' There was the thud of a man's shoe as a door was opened, then the flight of a man's white evening jacket, unmistakably Simon's. 'Get out and stay out!'

'I renounce every year I spent with you!' Simon strode out into the corridor in his shirt and trousers, red in the face, shouting hoarsely, 'You're not the woman I knew, or the woman I loved!'

Christie just stood there, staring at them, feeling hurt, humiliated, betrayed. Simon had obviously been making love to Nessa, right there, in Nessa's bedroom, where it could hardly have happened spontaneously.

'No, that's right, I'm not the woman you knew!' Nessa threw his other shoe at him with a noisy clatter, just missing him as he swore furiously and ducked. 'I'm the star you made me into! Nessa Vale—I created her! Isn't that what you used to boast? Well, go and boast it about Christie McCall! She obviously thinks——'

Christie slipped into her own bedroom silently, not wanting to hear any more. Closing the door, she leant on it, trembling with the deep sense of betrayal.

Of course she had felt guilty herself for betraying Simon on the beach with Jared—but that had been a genuine accident. Simon had quite obviously gone to Nessa's bedroom with her. What other reason could there have been but to betray Christie?

Some friend, she thought, staring down at her engagement ring. Some future husband.

But suddenly she found herself thinking, Why did I betray Simon with Jared? Because I was still in love with him, provoked beyond endurance, and ended up in an unexpected but very passionate kiss...

The shock hit her right between the eyes—Simon was in love with Nessa Vale. But that had to mean their involvement was even more deep than Simon had let on. So he had not only betrayed her tonight—he had lied to her about Nessa. How long had he really known the actress? It must have been a great deal of time, or he wouldn't have said, 'I renounce you...you're not the woman I knew...loved...'

Just the memory of the passion in his voice made her shake her head in disbelief. A visual image of him and Nessa making love leapt into her mind, and she was astonished to realise she felt no jealousy: the idea of Simon sprawled in feverish desire on Nessa was slightly incongruous, but it wasn't unbearably hurtful.

Moving to her bed, she sank on to it, toying with her silk nightgown in one slim hand as she frowned thought-

fully. Suddenly she remembered all his remarks about
how dangerous grand passion was. Obviously, Nessa Vale
was his grand passion, and always had been.

A deep loyalty to Simon tore her away from thoughts
of betrayal. If he loved Nessa—what right did she have
to try and stand in his way? Apart from that, she herself
had been guilty of betrayal, even if it had been un-
planned and accidental. One couldn't stop passion rising
any more than one could stop the earth revolving around
the sun. How could she either blame or berate Simon
for being human enough to love, feel passion, and
stumble into betrayal?

Getting undressed, she slid into bed, her thoughts
turning back to Jared, and the love that had exploded
so passionately between them on the beach. Would he
go straight to Nessa tonight? Jealousy shot through her
like white-hot fire and she veered away from it, screaming
silently. It was nothing like the way she'd felt when she
imagined Simon making love to Nessa Vale.

Maybe I don't care as much for Simon as I thought
I did, she realised as she slid down, turning out the light,
and, as soon as she was in darkness, her mind turned
back to Jared, the man she loved.

She was angry and hurt that he had told her he wanted
her on the casting couch. But she was also aware that
he wouldn't get what he wanted, as he would find out
tomorrow morning, when she told Mike Camarra that
she was going to reject the role.

Pain lit her blue eyes as she stared into the silent
darkness of her bedroom, the only sound that of the fan
whirring softly overhead, keeping the heat of the
California night at bay.

What lay in the future now? Would she ever find love?
Would she ever be a truly great star? What would happen
to the future she had planned with her beloved friend,

Simon, who had just betrayed her with the woman he obviously loved?

And would Jared ever forgive her her ambition...?

Next day, she woke from a searingly intense dream of Jared making love to her, and realised it was because he had reawoken the sleeping seductress in her body, made her burn with reawakened desire for his body.

Quickly, she pushed back the duvet, went to the bathroom and determinedly took a cold shower. No dreams of love or lovemaking today, she reminded herself sternly. If she was to survive this weekend, she would have to be businesslike, down-to-earth and very professional. Mike Camarra was a ruthless shark. She would have to make an appointment with him for this morning, and give him the news formally, making it absolutely clear she was not going to be talked out of her decision.

Later, she dressed in white jeans and a white lace top, then went downstairs to find everyone sunning themselves at breakfast out by the glittering, hot blue pool.

'Morning!' Mike Camarra welcomed, standing by the barbecue where fresh meat and fish were being cooked in the open air. 'Cooked breakfast or just a coffee and Danish?'

She walked coolly over to him. 'Isn't there any fruit?'

'Plenty.' He drew on his cigar, gestured to a large table groaning under fruit, rolls, et cetera. 'How did your chat with Jared go last night?'

'Oh...' She hesitated, aware of the others listening in the hot sunlight. 'Well, I'd like to have a word with you about that later, Mike. Would you mind if I requested an appointment? Some time this morning? In your study?'

Mike looked at her with a frown for a long moment, then gave a slow shrug. 'Sure. Why not? Eleven suit you?'

'That's perfect,' she said, because it gave her time to talk to Simon and break the news of her decision to him.

Mike frowned, flipped a swordfish steak over, every inch the rich movie mogul in dark blue silk robe, dark blue shorts, tanned paunch and grey-haired chest, his eyes hidden behind dark glasses. 'Nothing went badly wrong last night, I take it? I mean—you are old friends, right? I'm sure I remember Jared telling me you'd known each other since way back when . . .'

'Maybe she's forgotten,' Jared's cynical voice drawled suddenly, and she spun to stare angrily at him, her heart thudding.

Mike waved cheerfully in greeting. 'Morning, Jared! Sleep well?'

'In fits and starts,' Jared said, striding across to the breakfast area, sexy in jeans and a black tight-fitting T-shirt, dark eyes flashing contemptuously over Christie. 'Must have been the champagne.'

'At least it was vintage,' Mike laughed. 'Fancy a swordfish for breakfast?'

Jared frowned, peering at the grill. 'Any chance of home fries with it?'

'A man after my own heart!' Mike clapped him on the back, chewed his cigar over to one corner of his mouth, and called out, 'Rosita! Get this man some home fries!'

'*Si*, Señor Camarra!' The dusky beauty bobbed a curtsy.

Jared looked at Christie. She looked back at him. Her eyes were hidden by dark glasses, but they blazed with love and anger, her face tightening with pride as she lifted her blonde head, almost in challenge. He might despise her now, but he would feel very differently after she had had her meeting with Mike Camarra.

'How about you, Chris?' Jared asked sardonically. 'Pleasant dreams—or unpleasant?'

'Very pleasant indeed,' she replied swiftly, lifting her blonde brows, still keeping that look of challenge on her beautiful face.

Jared frowned, obviously disbelieving.

'In fact,' Christie said with a smile, 'I feel better than I have done for years. Marvellous. Full of hope for the future.'

His hard mouth parted in shock.

'That was a pretty speech!' Mike Camarra laughed, flipping a waffle. 'Anything to do with your meeting with me at eleven?'

'Meeting?' Jared's dark brows jerked together.

'Sure,' Mike drawled, obviously aware that something was rotten in the state of California today, and that he was interfering with passionate undercurrents. 'We're getting together very formally indeed, aren't we, honey? In my office, eleven sharp.'

'Anything to do with *Tigresse*?' Jared bit out under his breath, glaring at Christie. 'If so, it should come to my attention as director. Unless you want to see Mike in his capacity as head of the studio...?'

Christie lifted her brows, and said softly, 'That's nothing to do with you, Jared. Mike is my boss. I often have formal meetings with——'

A heavy brass ornament suddenly sailed out of a bedroom balcony window on the east wing and crashed on to the terrace, fifty yards away.

'Hey!' Mike shouted angrily up at the hot balcony. 'You can pay for that, whoever threw it! My wife bought it in Japan last——'

'Sorry, Mike!' Nessa stormed on to the balcony like Joan Crawford in a white satin fur-trimmed négligé, her eyes spitting fire. 'I'm just trying to get an uninvited guest out of my bedroom!'

There was the distant slam of a door.

Nessa disappeared from the balcony.

'Never a dull moment,' Mike commented wryly.

'Passionate pair, aren't they?' Millie called from the table she sat at a few yards away, beneath a gaily-fringed parasol with Bobby Datchett, the notorious Hollywood womaniser of the last thirty years. 'Do you remember the first night we met them, Mike? Nessa broke every single piece of crockery on the dining-table, just because Simon said he didn't like the dinner she'd served.'

Christie flushed, angrily aware that everyone was grinning at her, and that she now looked very much like the betrayed fiancé. It was, of course, humiliating. Suddenly, she realised that Millie had known it was Simon in Nessa's room, and also that she had known Simon and Nessa were a couple...

How long had it really been going on, then? she wondered in shock, staring up at the deserted sun-bleached balcony, the palm trees towering beside it into a halcyon blue sky.

'Stop staring like that,' Jared murmured, stepping beside her suddenly, his voice low enough only for her to hear as he took her arm. 'Everyone knows what's between those two—don't let them see how bad you feel about their love affair, or——'

Her head turned as she gasped, staring. 'You *knew*?'

'Of course!' He frowned, his voice still low. 'They were one of the most famous couples in Hollywood. Don't tell me *you* didn't know?' His sharp eyes noticed the humiliated flush on her face. 'Oh, great. So Simon's even worse than you are when it comes to amoral——'

'Mind your own business!' she snapped under her breath. 'Simon just wanted to forget her, that's all. He didn't know she'd be here.'

'Any more than I knew you'd be here.' He studied her, eyes narrowing, and gave a terse nod. 'Yes, I guess we're all in the same rocky old boat. Come on, get some breakfast and sit down. I want to talk to you.'

Christie angrily let him lead her to the fruit table, not wanting to cause a scene in front of the others. She chose melon and blueberries, then walked with Jared to the table farthest from the others, closest to the inviting, cool blue waters of the swimming pool.

'So what's this meeting with Mike?' Jared demanded when they were seated beneath the fringed parasol. 'Are you thinking of telling him about my four-poster casting couch? If so, Christie, I warn you——'

'Don't be ridiculous!' she said flatly. 'I wouldn't be such a fool. Mike's been around, he's no stranger to Hollywood immorality. I expect he'd just smile if I told him you'd demanded sex in exchange for the role!'

Jared leaned back, eyes narrowing. 'So what's the plan?'

She ate a blueberry and did not reply.

'Come on! I know you only just arranged it with him, because otherwise he'd have told me about it last night! It must have something to do with our argument on the beach. So what is it? Tell me, or——'

'I'm going to refuse the role of Lelie,' she said unsteadily, and ate another blueberry in the stunned silence that followed.

He was leaning back in the chair, utterly frozen, his eyes wiped clean of expression. All around them crickets buzzed in the gardens, and a little multi-coloured dragonfly flew across the swimming pool looking for lilies.

'Is this some kind of trick?' he demanded thickly.

'No trick.'

'Come off it, Chris!' He sounded sure of himself, but his voice was rough with shock. 'You'd sell your soul to the devil for that part!'

'Apparently not,' she said huskily. 'I certainly draw the line at selling my body to you—and you're only a close relation of the Prince of Darkness.'

'Nice to know you've got my measure at last!' he bit out thickly, and leaned forwards, powerful hair-roughened forearms on the table, the glitter of his wrist-watch dazzling as the sunlight caught it. 'But don't think for one second that I believe you really intend to refuse the role of Lelie, because I remember only too well your excitable words last night! How it was going to fulfil all your dreams, give you everything you wanted, give you——'

'Morning, Simon!' Millie called into the centre of their heated conversation.

They both looked round instantly to see Simon walking stiffly across the terrace with an unmistakable black eye.

'Oh, my God . . .!' Christie was on her feet at once, appalled as she went across to him. He saw her and flushed dark red, punching himself briefly and oddly in the arm, then clutching it for a long moment. The bruise around his eye must have been made last night. It was livid purple with faint yellowing at the edges.

'Good morning, Christie,' Simon said thickly, his grey eyes blazing a warning to her not to show sympathy or concern or even to mention his black eye. 'I slept pleasantly. Did you?'

She stopped in front of him. 'Yes, I—I slept very well.'

'Good.' He nodded curtly, then turned to Mike. 'A swordfish steak, if you please, Mike.'

'Oh, that Ivy League accent,' Mike said with a grin much like the ex-swordfish.

'Your home fries, *señor*!' Rosita was suddenly walking across to Jared with a plate of fresh cooked home fries.

Simon looked at Christie. 'Where are you sitting, darling?'

'Over there,' she said huskily. 'With Jared. Come on, I'd be delighted if you'd join us, darling.'

Together, they began to walk across the hot stone terrace to the table where Jared sat watching them with hard, narrowed eyes and a tight-lipped expression.

'Isn't Nessa coming down yet, Simon?' Millie called gaily.

'I wouldn't know!' he replied stiffly.

'Too busy ducking the guided missiles, huh?' Bobby Datchett called, laughing like mad and clapping his hand. 'Violence, violence!'

Simon carried on walking rigidly to the table, where he and Jared glared at each other, both bristling with male aggression.

'Love the eye make-up,' Jared drawled mockingly as Simon sat down. 'I understand my girlfriend applied it for you?'

Christie's heart soared with sudden acid jealousy, her face whitening as she stared at him, thinking, Oh, God, please stop me feeling this, stop me loving Jared, stop me going crazy with all this unwanted passion.

Simon didn't reply to Jared's taunt, but instead began to eat his steak while Christie poured him some orange juice, her hand shaking as she thought of Jared's hard, male body moving passionately between Nessa's slim white thighs. Damn him to hell! She put the orange juice down, jealousy shooting through her veins. He's ruining my career and I'm powerless to prevent him. And the worst part was that she knew she still secretly, stupidly hoped that he might love her again once he found out she was serious about refusing the part.

Her eyes flicked to his tough, handsome face. He had been so sincere last night. So loving, so trusting—surely he couldn't be seriously involved with Nessa Vale, any more than she herself was seriously involved with Simon? She had to believe that, or would never make it through this weekend with her self-respect intact. The only other option she had was to believe that Jared was a snake, a rat, and a promiscuous cheat, and if she believed that, even for one second, she would despise herself for being so deeply in love with him.

Suddenly, she saw the heart of Jared's dilemma more clearly than she ever had. Was that how he felt about her? Oh, God, let it be that, because, if it was, he would surely change his mind once he knew she had refused to do the picture. And then, hot on the heels of that thought, the one that had eluded her since last night—had Jared felt no other option but to throw her in at the deep end? Was his casting couch demand just a test? If it was, she was about to pass it with flying colours, and, all career ambitions aside, it made no difference whether it was a test, a spontaneous impulse, a ruthless desire for sexual revenge or an act of self-defence from a man who had been bitterly hurt. The fact was that she could not accept it and would, therefore, have to refuse the role. Arguing with that inside herself would only cause her further pain. The best thing to do was just accept it, stand by her decision, and see it through. Then leave love in the lap of the gods...

She hoped they would reward her integrity and courage.

'Christie,' Jared said tightly, watching her with narrowed eyes. 'I'd like to have a word in private with you. After your meeting with Mike. Shall we say—midday, in my bedroom?'

Simon looked up, baffled. 'What meeting with——?'

'I don't think your bedroom is an appropriate place to discuss business, Jared,' Christie cut in coolly. 'Shall we instead meet at midday in the drawing-room?'

Jared's mouth twisted in a cynical smile. 'Fine! There are plenty of couches in there, just perfect for casting!' Getting to his feet, he treated her to a contemptuous look before striding away to the barbecue area, leaving his home fries and swordfish steak barely eaten.

Christie watched him go with hungry eyes, her heart thudding at the prospect of that meeting. How would he react? He had obviously made it midday so he could speak to Mike before he saw her, and that was confirmed now by the fact that he stood talking to Mike by the barbecue in what was obviously a serious business discussion. Oh, how she prayed he would rediscover his love for her, as he had done last night, before she made that fatal error.

'What on earth is going on?' Simon asked under his breath. 'What are all these meetings for?'

She turned to him, took a deep breath, and said, 'Simon, prepare yourself for a shock. I'm going to refuse the role of Tigresse.'

He dropped his knife and fork with a clatter. 'What!'

'Don't even think about trying to talk me out of it.' Her face was strong, determined. 'And don't ask me why I've made the decision. The only thing you need to know is that I *have* made it, and that nothing you do or say can change my mind.'

He stared at her. 'But...this is simply absurd, Christie! You're surely not cancelling the biggest opportunity of your career, just because of Jared Buchanan, are you?'

'Yes,' she admitted thickly. 'But it's not for the reasons you think, and I'm certainly not prepared to tell you what the real reasons are.'

'But you must tell me, Christie! Not only am I your agent, but I'm your fiancé!'

She arched blonde brows. 'I might say the same to you about that black eye you're sporting.'

He went red, lowering his lashes. 'I...'

Silence trailed between them. Birds were singing in the open air all around them, and the sweet scent of the Pacific was mingling with the scent of barbecued meat.

'There's a lot more to your relationship with Nessa than meets the eye,' Christie said under her breath. 'I'm not going to pry, Simon, because I can see you're going through hell.'

Clumsily, he drank some orange juice, avoiding her eyes.

'But you should have told me about her long before you asked me to marry you.' She studied him from behind dark glasses. 'It casts very grave doubts on our marriage. How can we hope to stay together for a lifetime when you've quite obviously omitted to tell me about the most important love relationship of your past?'

'I can see,' he said thickly, lifting grey, guilt-ridden eyes to hers, 'that I've been selfish and stupid about it. I should have told you a long time ago, but—I couldn't bring myself to. She humiliated me, you see, Christie. She destroyed me in front of all Hollywood, and it wasn't until you won your Oscar that I was able to even contemplate facing her again, let alone talking about her.'

She listened in amazement, suddenly realising why everyone including Jared seemed to know all about Nessa and Simon, too. 'My God . . . so you split up just before you came to England and found me?'

'Yes,' he said bitterly. 'That's why I always thought someone else would tell you about us. It was such a big story, you see. Nessa made me the laughing-stock of this town, and I ran away to England to recover. That's the truth of it, and I can't blame Ness for continually pointing it out to me with such anger.' He gingerly touched his black eye, and gave a husky laugh. 'She always was a very tempestuous star!'

'How long have you known Nessa Vale?'

'Oh . . .' Simon looked anxious. 'All my life.'

She sucked in her breath. 'What!'

'Christie, we were brought up together. Nessa was the girl next door.' He laughed unsteadily. 'As close to next door as you can get on Long Island, and we were both from wealthy families, lived in big houses, went to the same birthday parties . . . that kind of thing.'

'Simon, this is incredible!' She was staring at him in amazement. 'How could you have omitted to tell me this?'

He raked a hand through his ash-blond hair, looking miserable. 'I couldn't bear to be reminded of her. Not when I first met you. I'd built Nessa into a big star, then stupidly went around boasting about how I'd created her!'

She studied him with incredulous eyes. 'And she didn't like it?'

'No. In fact, I was even worse than that. I actually told people that without me she'd be nothing. She heard about it, and threatened to fire me. Me!' He laughed bitterly. 'Her childhood sweetheart, the boy next door, the man who'd devoted his life to her!'

Trying to ignore the sense of alienation she felt at those words, Christie reminded herself that she had a similar undying passion for Jared, and asked calmly, 'Did she fire you?'

'No, but I was so incensed by the threat that I did something really stupid. I started to take her biggest rival at that time, Sally Harker, out on the town. Made it look like a red-hot affair. Got myself in the gossip columns with Sally, and ridiculed Nessa.'

'Oh, my God . . . you fool . . .'

'I'm afraid so,' he said thickly. 'Nessa fired me and switched to *my* biggest rival, another agent working closely with Camarra Pictures. I felt absolutely gutted, Christie. I didn't believe she'd do it. I tried to see her, to explain that I hadn't really had an affair with Sally Harker, but—well, you can imagine how that meeting ended. Flying ornaments, slamming doors and a lot of high-pitched screaming. I slunk away to lick my wounds, then tried to see her again. I found the new agent wandering around her apartment in his dressing-gown. He was obviously her new lover, and everybody knew it, too.'

Christie closed her eyes, sighing deeply. 'What a horror story... why do people do these things to each other?'

'"The heart has its reasons which reason knows nothing of",' he said softly, and the quote from Pascal reminded her of her days at drama school, of Masterclass on a Friday afternoon, and her dreams of being famous, of reaching the pinnacle of acting acclaim. Today, those dreams were to be destroyed as she refused the part of Lelie.

The funniest thing was that all she cared about was what Jared would think when he found out.

'Yes,' she said, laughing suddenly at her own madness, 'the heart does have reasons which reason definitely knows nothing of! So don't you worry about your crazy love for Nessa Vale, Simon. It may cast grave doubts on our prospects for marriage, but at least it means you're human, and alive, and capable of Grand Passion.'

He looked wry. 'You were beginning to wonder, were you?'

'Sometimes.' She gave a deep sigh. 'And maybe this is all fate in some strange way. Maybe we're not really meant to get married. We were discussing it on the way here—remember? Desperately trying to make excuses for why we were still only friends, and not lovers.'

'Are you saying you want to call off our engagement, too?' he asked thickly. 'I—I'll understand if you do, but please don't make it public yet. Not with all this going on, Nessa here to witness it and——'

'Oh, don't worry.' She touched his hand reassuringly. 'I won't tell anyone it's officially over. Not until we leave Casa Camarra and can make a quiet little statement to the Press. We'll say it's a mutual agreement reached amicably, and that you'll continue to represent me professionally.'

He nodded slowly, squeezing her hand. 'Thanks, Christie. I don't know what to say. It's so good of you to be so understanding, and so forgiving of my very selfish behaviour over Nessa.'

'Not at all,' she said huskily, pulses leaping as she flicked her gaze across to the powerful figure of Jared Buchanan standing talking to Mike. 'I have problems of my own...'

CHAPTER SEVEN

AT SOME point over the next fifteen minutes, Mike Camarra disappeared inside the house. Jared was immediately buttonholed by a nubile young starlet, who pouted and posed as she flirted with him in her pretty pink bikini, making Christie's eyes narrow with a tinge of fiery jealousy. He had enough women fighting for his attention right now. He hardly needed the nubile starlet to add her name to the list. Besides, she thought irritably, the girl was too young for Jared, only seventeen and half-witted with it. Christie could tell he thought so too, by the wry way his dark eyes flickered over the starlet's body, and the hard indulgent smile on his tough mouth.

Jared liked sexy women, but he liked them with brains, and he liked them to be his equal. Or did he? Christie frowned, watching him across the hot terrace. Was that one of the reasons their relationship had fallen apart? Because Christie had not truly been his professional equal when they had first met? OK, she had always had the dream and the potential to stand alongside him, but, back then, there was no real proof of that.

It seemed suddenly important to find out, now that they were poised to come face to face, for the first time, as true equals. Once Jared found out she had rejected the role of Tigresse, he would find the barriers falling from around Christie, like the thorns around Sleeping Beauty's castle, just melting away like magic, bringing the sunlight back as fear, anger and mistrust disappeared. What would he do then? she wondered.

Her heart skipped and jumped at the thought of finally meeting Jared on level ground, after all this time. She was no longer a struggling bit-part actress in a little-known soap. She was an internationally famous Academy Award-winning film actress now, and Jared's illusions about the perfect wife and mother had been shattered along with his illusions that she would gladly give up her career for him.

Would it really change his mind forever towards her when he found out she'd rejected Lelie? She prayed it would, because rediscovering her love for him had suddenly given her life the kind of fulfilment that had been missing for so long, and which had begun to gnaw at her, bringing emptiness and self-doubt as she gathered trophies but no hugs.

Tears stung her eyes. A hug...such a simple thing. Why was it so difficult? Especially for an ambitious woman. She realised suddenly that she had been channelling her drive into her career, and that her feelings had been swept aside for years to help her reach her goal.

Not just years, but probably all her life. The sad, hurt, angry child she had been had needed the protection that only massive success could bring. But the truth was— she had needed love.

Everything seemed so clear to her suddenly. All her life she had been looking for success when what she needed was love. When she met Jared she found that love, briefly, but was too immature really to take it, too hungry for success still to let herself be just a woman.

Jared had tried to stand in the way of her ambition, but he had done that for his own reasons, and the sad irony was that they were almost identical reasons to her own: he had been hungry for his own childhood illusions. That longing for a perfect woman was as deeply embedded in Jared's childhood as Christie's longing for massive global fame.

Everything would be all right if they could just get it.

What nonsense, she thought with a wry smile. It was like believing that everything would be all right if you were a dress size smaller. Or if you owned a red Ferrari. Or if the moon turned to blue cheese.

The truth was, everything had to be all right now, and the only way that was possible was if you fulfilled yourself in every single area. Not just career, money and prestige, but in the realm of the heart and the senses too. What else did fulfilment mean, but quite literally to fulfil? And she wasn't just a film star—she was a woman, too.

It seemed incredible to her now to look back on her life and see so clearly that she had been unfulfilled as a woman for most of it. In all the joy of career fulfilment, she had ignored her feminine instincts at their deepest roots. In many ways, like Sleeping Beauty, she had been lying in the topmost turret room of her self, gathering dust, for years, and, as she faced that astonishing truth, she realised that her growing sense of emptiness recently was nothing more or less than the Sleeping Beauty within screaming for attention, love, fulfilment.

Funny that she should reach this final conclusion now, at the height of her fame. But how else could it have been reached? There was no point saying she had done it all 'wrong', because she hadn't. She had been driven to high achievement, just as Jared had. And she had needed to reach the top, see her dreams come true, and explode the myth—before she could recognise what she had been rigorously suppressing.

She looked across at Jared and prayed that he had exploded his myths too, in the only way possible: by living them.

Suddenly, looking at him here in the hot sunlight, she wanted his children so badly she could taste it, could feel herself getting ready for pregnancy, and the funniest thing was that she no longer saw pregnancy as something to put off until later, or as something that might spoil her movie-star figure—she saw it as the most natural thing in the world. And for the first time in her life she felt at one with nature, with the birds singing in the hot California morning, the crickets chirping softly in the vivid green shrubs, the gentle wave of the palm trees against the blue, blue sky.

If Jared didn't really love her, and if she gave up *Tigresse* for nothing, she would lose the beauty of this brief, shining moment for ever. But her ambition and her emotional needs had been causing deep conflict in her life for too long. She could not ignore the screams from that top turret room any longer. Certainly not when Jared had her backed into the toughest corner of her life.

'It's almost eleven,' Simon said beside her.

She turned with a start. 'Oh . . .' Her stomach tensed with nerves at the thought of what she had to do.

'Better hurry.' Simon tapped his watch. 'Mike Camarra doesn't like to be kept waiting.'

Christie got to her feet, her blonde head held high as she walked with her sensual, animalistic sway in white jeans and lace top, across the hot stone terrace area to the house.

Jared watched her every move, still talking to the nubile starlet, but his eyes flicked to and fro, following Christie every step of the way, and she burned with the thrill of his attention, particularly as it was so obviously obliterating the charms of that pretty little starlet.

Plenty of men ahead for you, little starlet, she thought with a wry smile, but only one for me, so keep your hands off him!

Rosita directed her to Mike's office inside the mansion. Seconds later, she was outside the oak door, summoning all her courage and professional skills as she knocked sharply on it.

'Come!' Mike shouted.

She went inside, and found him lounging behind an impressive desk in an oak-panelled room with a big red leather couch and swivel chairs, books on cinema lining the walls, telephones, a fax, a computer on the desk, and a big cigar clenched firmly between his teeth.

'Sit down, Christie,' Mike drawled with a slow smile. 'And tell me what's on your mind.'

She closed the door, removed her sunglasses, swayed over to the swivel chair opposite the desk, and sank down into it. As soon as she was settled, she just told him the truth straight out. He listened impassively, hands behind grey head, chewing on his cigar.

'I see,' he said when she had finished. 'And you don't want to tell me precisely why you've come to this decision?'

'As I say—it's a decision I've made for personal reasons.'

'Because you were once romantically involved with Jared Buchanan,' he stated flatly and switched the cigar to the other side of his mouth.

She felt herself colour hotly. 'Yes.'

'But if you were romantically involved,' he drawled, 'why is it impossible for you to work together? You can't say you hate each other. You've spent almost all your time with Jared since you got here. And by the way—I saw you coming in last night with sand all over your dress.'

Her flush deepened.

Mike grinned at her, eyes glittering metallic blue. 'Don't worry. I won't tell anyone you were making it with Jared on the beach!' His smile broadened as he saw her embarrassment. 'But if you're capable of getting in a lovesexy situation so quickly—surely you must get on just a little?'

'No,' she said thickly. 'We argue a lot, Mike. It would be a very fiery working relationship, if it worked at all.'

His eyes narrowed. 'You mean you're still in love.'

The blunt statement of fact made her face burn scarlet, but she could not reply, just lowered her lashes to hide the passionate flare in her eyes. He would undoubtedly tell Jared about this conversation, so anything that was said might just as well be said in his presence.

'Well, that's good,' Mike drawled with a smile. 'We can work on that. We can build on it.'

'Mike...' She looked up, angry determination in her eyes. 'I mean what I say. I don't wish to make this film with Jared Buchanan.'

'Oh, don't worry.' He held up a fat, ringed hand. 'I accept your decision as final, and I'm not going to hold it against you professionally. I know you've always done your best for Camarra, and I know the right picture will make you an even more bankable star.'

The relief almost made her faint.

'But...' He directed one finger towards her. 'I still have you pencilled in for *Tigresse*, and I'm going to keep you pencilled in for the rest of the weekend. If, by the time we all go back to Beverly Hills tomorrow night, you still want to cancel your opportunity to play *Tigresse*...' He shrugged. 'I'll just look for another vehicle for you and recast *Tigresse*.'

'Thank you, Mike!' she said in astonishment, staring at him, barely able to believe he had been not only so understandingly calm, but also so very generous.

'Don't mention it, honey,' he replied with a lazy smile. 'Just keep thinking about it until tomorrow night. Oh— and work on that relationship with Jared. Maybe take him down to the beach again tonight!'

Christie went scarlet again, her mouth tightening as she looked away and said, 'I'll certainly think about *Tigresse*, Mike, but I want you to remember, the chances of me reconsidering are almost a thousand to one!'

As she left the oak-panelled study, he was already on the phone to Hollywood. Christie felt weak with relief as she walked along the marble corridors back to the main hallway. It had been the hardest decision of her professional life, but thank God she had found an understanding boss in Mike Camarra. He had made a number of personal remarks, and she didn't like them, but she knew he was that kind of a guy, and he had at least given her the opportunity to change her mind if she wanted. He wasn't to know Jared had proposed a casting couch solution that she had found unacceptable. And from what Jared had said that morning out by the pool, he wouldn't tell Mike either.

The cool marble hallway was filled with sunlight and the suggestion of a hot day outside. The chandeliers swung gently in the breeze from the fans. Jean Harlow was smiling in a way which suggested a wisecrack from her sassy red lips at any moment. Christie looked at her in admiration and believed she could still one day get there as an oil painting of a previous famous guest at Casa Camarra. A smile lit her eyes. They moved on up to Vivien Leigh, haughtily beautiful, cruelly beautiful, just plain beautiful . . .

'Dreaming ambitious dreams?' Jared's dark voice drawled behind her.

She spun with a gasp to see him standing in the vast sunlit doorway like a stark silhouette of male power.

'You'll never get there,' he said coolly, 'if you really did just go in and refuse the lead role in *Tigresse*.'

'Oh, yes, I will, Jared.' She lifted her blonde head. 'You just wait and see.' Turning, she walked up the sweeping red staircase with an excited, half-fearful smile, aware of his dark eyes narrowed with angry admiration on her as she moved, and even more deeply aware that he was now on his way to see Mike Camarra and discover the truth.

Inside her bedroom, she closed the door and suddenly couldn't bear the wait. Her pulses were jumping like wildfire at the thought of her future. What a decision, what a momentous day...

Her future, yesterday so dry, sealed and certain, was now spinning in the air like a silver dollar, and she could only hold her breath as she waited for it to land—heads, she won. She won everything—everything. The man, the love, the children. The home, the fun, the family. The fame, the glory, the wonderful, glittering partnership with a man she loved and respected...

But if that dollar landed tails side up—she lost everything. Mike Camarra had said he would find her another vehicle and continue to build her career, but the truth was, roles like Tigresse didn't come along every day, and no matter what he said now, if there ever came a time when she starred in two flops in a row, Mike Camarra would drop her like a hot potato. Simon would stop being her agent, if that time ever came, for friendship went by the board in Hollywood when professional reputation, and more to the point—that great god, Money— were at stake.

As for Jared... she closed her eyes in horror at the thought of how quickly he could desert her once he found out she'd refused the role of Tigresse. After all, hadn't he stayed away from her all this time? He could have approached her at any point in the last three years. Perhaps his only interest in her this time had been sexual power combined with a dynamite sure-fire winner at the box-office.

Again, that painful dilemma was revealed to her. Jared might not be the knight in shining armour she had pinned her hopes on. He might be a rotten, corrupt bastard. He might be Nessa's casual lover. He might be seducing that nubile starlet on the quiet. He might be using Christie's past relationship with him in order to manipulate her on to the casting couch. He might, at the end of the day, be Mr Wrong.

The full impact of what she was facing suddenly hit her.

It was at that moment that there was a knock on the door.

Almost jumping out of her skin, she stood listening to her heart hammering violently for a split-second before calling out, 'Come in!'

The door opened, and it was Jared, as she had known it would be, shouldering into the doorway in that black T-shirt, tanned arms bulging with muscles, narrow hips as lean and sexy as his long legs in those faded blue jeans.

'I just spoke to Mike,' he said expressionlessly, and closed the door.

Christie had never been so excited and afraid in her whole life. She was dry-mouthed, her stomach churning with butterflies, her legs weak beneath her.

'And?' she asked, summoning her last strength, lifting her blonde head, ready to take it on the jaw if she had to.

'And...' He gave a rough laugh, his eyes bitterly cynical. 'Don't think you've got me fooled for one second! I know this is all part of some long-term plan to get the role and bypass the casting couch. I haven't figured out yet how you're planning to do it, but give me a while, Christie, and I'll get there!'

Her heart plummeted, seemed to slide right out of her stomach as she realised she had lost her gamble, lost it hands down, lost her love, her man, her unborn sons with dark hair and dark eyes and obsessive talent.

She swayed as though she was about to fall.

Jared moved towards her instantly, then stopped as she recovered her balance. His mouth twisted with anger. 'I should have known you weren't on the verge of fainting from shock!'

'Jared,' she said in a sickly voice, 'I can't believe you still think I'm a carbon copy of Lelie, ready to do anything just to get——'

'Come on!' he replied tightly. 'You gambled and lost! Don't try to drag the performance out for my benefit. You should know I'm not going to believe a word you say.'

'Don't be so blind, Jared. Don't be so obstinate!' Her voice was shaking with disbelief. 'I've refused the role! What more can I do?'

'Well, quite,' he said sardonically. 'I've been trying to guess precisely what more you can do, but even I have trouble keeping up with the convoluted way your mind works, so I've come here to ask you point-blank what the hell your next move is.'

'My next move...' She stared, shaking her head, bitterly hurt and at a loss as to what to do. 'Jared, I've always been ambitious, but I really do draw the line at the casting couch. That's all there is to it. You want me to jump into bed and—and play Salome to your Herod, but I won't do it. I just won't do it and there's no other reason behind my——'

'No other reason!' He laughed derisively.

'What other reason could there be!'

'A game strategy! Some new plot to——'

'Don't be ridiculous, what kind of woman do you think I am!'

'Dangerous!' he said hoarsely, striding towards her suddenly, making her back with a gasp as she saw the extent of the rage in his dark eyes. 'I've never recovered from trusting you, and I doubt if I ever will! I almost got suckered into it again last night, but I certainly don't intend to make the same mistake twice!'

'Jared, I refused the casting couch,' she said breathlessly as he cornered her against the dressing-table. 'Please believe me, please——'

'Liar!' His strong hands gripped her shoulders. 'You're nothing but a lethal little black widow. I could tangle spiders in the webs you weave, and you're not weaving another one around me! You're getting on the casting couch and giving the performance of your life—with or without the role of Lelie as a reward!'

'No!' she cried, but he was too angry, passion blazing in his eyes as he dragged her towards the bed. 'No! Jared, for God's sake!'

'For my sake, Christie!' he said hoarsely, pulling her down on to the bed with him, his body rolling on top of hers, trapping her beneath him as he stared down with tortured eyes. 'For my sake! I can't take it any more! Fighting you, going through hell because I know I'll never get what I really want—to have you, to truly possess you—any more than I did three years ago. The only thing I can take is power over you...' His voice roughened. 'But you just smashed even that from my grasp, didn't you?'

'I didn't do it for that reason!' she whispered, her heart banging hard with fear and excitement as she lay there on the bed beneath him, as vulnerable with love as she ever had been, suddenly not caring how or why they had ended up lying there together while he declared his obsession with such dark, dangerous passion, caring only that they were there, that it felt good, and that no matter how much he raged against her he was still obsessed, even if it was with desire for her sexual surrender. At least it was obsession, just as she was obsessed, loving every inch of him, and of his fiery passion. 'I did it because I can't go on the casting couch. I never have for any director, Jared.'

'Don't tell me those articles were lies again!' he said roughly, hands tightening on her body. 'I don't want to hear the sincerity in your voice because I believe it . . .'

'Then why don't you believe my reasons for turning *Tigresse* down?'

His mouth tightened. 'Because I want revenge on you! I hate myself for it, I hate you for making me feel that way, but it *is* how I feel, and only one thing can ease it for me!'

Her heart beat with abrupt violence. 'Jared . . .' she whispered on an involuntary note of alarmed excitement.

'I keep thinking of the powerful release it would bring me,' he said thickly, and bent his dark head, his hot mouth burning over her throat, making her shiver with absurd, irrational pleasure. 'Every muscle in my body wrenched free of tension . . . the release of pent-up emotion . . . and then the peace . . . oh, God, how I need to feel that peace, that freedom from obsession . . .'

'Would it last, though?' she whispered, her hands moving to his strong neck, caressing the locked muscles there and hearing him groan with extreme pleasure. 'Or would you roll away from me, Jared, minutes later, and start to hate me again?'

His heart thudded wildly as he whispered, 'I'll always hate you, but I'll never stop wanting you!'

She gave a little moan of breathless excitement. Her body shifted beneath his. Excitement was throbbing in her now, overwhelming her fears, her anger, her confused emotions. All that mattered was his hard body against hers, their joint obsession reaching explosion point—and there was so much more to fulfilment than a career.

He bent his head.

She arched to meet him.

They kissed fiercely, hungrily, their mouths almost eating each other. It was so swift, like fire flaring up from petrol and flint, while her arms wrapped around his strong neck and his hands moved fast over her body, fast, very fast, stroking her breasts, moving down to her waist even as she gasped and arched in pleasure against him, then down to her hips, her jean-clad thighs splayed invitingly for him.

He was unbuttoning her lace top with determined fingers. She raked and ruffled his black hair. He tore the top open, his mouth burned over her upper breast, and, as she cried out in rising torment, his hand tugged the lacy bra down to bare her breast fully and he suckled her with his hot mouth.

'I hate you!' he said raggedly, and his teeth grazed her erect nipple. 'I'd like to teach you a serious damned lesson in bed...'

'Oh, darling...' she heard her tortured voice say. 'Oh, yes, teach me a lesson...'

He groaned hoarsely, his mouth closed over hers, and he started pulling her lace top from her body, throwing it to the floor as she let him strip her, his ragged breathing exciting her unbearably as he unclipped her bra, threw it across the room, eyes blazing as he stared briefly down at her, naked to the waist, then started pulling at his black T-shirt until he, too, was stripped to the waist.

Christie ran her hands over his magnificent chest, whispering, 'I ought to torment you! That's what you want me to do, isn't it? So you can believe I'm like her, like Lelie...'

He breathed faster, his hands excitingly rough on her body. 'You are like her...you are...'

'I think of you at night...' she whispered tauntingly. 'I think of your body...'

'And I think of your inventive little seductress mind!' His mouth was burning over hers and his heart was pumping blood round his body at top speed. 'I think of how you seduced me...dressing up for me...driving me completely crazy...'

'Stockings and suspenders?' she whispered, licking his tongue, playing with his dark hair. 'A little French maid's outfit?'

'Oh, God!' He groaned heavily, kissing her deeper, his hands fondling her breasts faster. 'And you wonder why I find it easy to believe you're an amoral little whore!'

Stung, she whispered fiercely, 'They were love-games!'

'Play them again, Chris!' He raised his head and he was flushed dark red with desire. 'We can still play all of them. Can't we? One after the other, and at the end of it, you'll get the role of Lelie, you'll be a really big star, you'll——'

'You haven't listened to a word I've said—have you?' Her mouth was bruised from his kisses, and her body fiercely aroused, but he still hadn't understood, he still couldn't see that she was motivated in all this by love of him, real love not ambition. 'I refused the role of Lelie! And I won't play casting couch to get it back!'

'Then why are you lying here with me like this?'

'Because I couldn't stop myself!' she confessed bitterly. 'Any more than you could! Why is it right for you to leap on me uncontrollably and wrong for me to respond?'

'You know why!'

'Oh, yes!' she cried fiercely. 'Because I'm a woman and, therefore, I ought be be an innocent, quivering novice! I ought to be crying, No, Sir Jared! Don't touch me!'

'Shut up!'

'When what I really want is to be kissed by you!' Her eyes blazed fierce emotion. 'I haven't been made love to

by any man, ever, except you, Jared, and the last time
you made love to me was——'

'Three years ago,' he cut in thickly. 'All right—but
why should I believe you're serious? When you're doing
this? Playing unbearably sexy games with me? Taunting
me? Offering me exactly what you know I'll do anything
to get from you—when you know damned well you're
not going to give it to me!'

Her mouth trembled as she said bitterly, 'I—I didn't
think about what I was doing. I was too excited.'

'Don't try to slide out of it now!' he said with a harsh
laugh. 'It's too late! You're already on the casting couch,
bargaining with me for that role!'

Her gasp of disbelief made him laugh even more
harshly.

'Didn't you realise that, you little fool?' His eyes glittered with savage possession down at her. 'What did you
think this was—a romantic kiss between old friends? This
is the casting couch all right, and you're going to fulfil
your part of the bargain just as I'm going to fulfil mine!
You give me what I want; I'll give you what you want.
And what better audition could there be for that role?'
His long hand stroked her bare breast provocatively. 'A
role you're so perfectly suited for...'

CHAPTER EIGHT

HORROR flared in Christie's eyes as she realised the enormity of her mistake. She had responded passionately to him out of love, pent-up tension, and a need to feel his body next to hers. But she had never for one moment suspected that he saw this as the casting couch.

Did he expect her to start bargaining with him? Yes, she could see in his dark eyes that he did. He was watching her, his hand on her bare breast and a cynical smile on his mouth, waiting for her to agree to his terms.

She knew what those terms would be. Hadn't he already made it clear? He would want to play every love-game in the book with her, taking his revenge sexually, and she was horrified to realise the extent of his real hatred for her.

Jared truly believed she had used him three years ago, and that she had operated the whole time without conscience, morals or love. Now he wanted to do the same thing to her, to ease the pain of betrayal he so wrongly felt she had inflicted on him.

And the worst thing was that he was right; it would ease it. If he got what he was demanding, months of sex-play, any way he wanted it, all the rage and hatred he felt would be released systematically from his body with every nerve-shattering climax she gave him.

But it would leave him feeling empty, soulless and alone—to say nothing of what it would do to her. She didn't even want to think about what it would do to her. It was too horrible to contemplate.

121

'So?' Jared was watching the slow dawning of awareness on her shocked face. 'Are you ready to drop the act and start making terms? Or do you want to make it worse for yourself than it is already?'

'How can it be worse?' she asked bitterly. 'I think we've already reached the nadir of hell you're determined to put us through!'

He gave a sardonic laugh. 'Try not to be so melodramatic, sweetie. We both know the game is up. You gambled and lost. Why can't you just admit it?' His hand stroked her breast, his body pressed against her, and he was rigid with desire. 'I'm going to get very impatient if I can't have you soon. And then your career is going to be ruined.'

'That's what you think, Jared!' Her eyes flared with angry pride. 'You've made that mistake all the way along the line! Three years ago you told me I couldn't make it in Hollywood—and I proved you wrong. Now you're trying to tell me I can't go on without you—and I'll prove you wrong on that score, too!'

'Go ahead and try!' he drawled tightly. 'I'll send you a couple of dimes on skid row!'

'I'll never be on skid row!' she said furiously. 'Or didn't Mike tell you? Oh, yes, that's right, Jared! He's not going to turn against me just because I refused *Tigresse*! He's going to find another—what was it now? Oh, yes! Another star vehicle for me!' Her blue eyes warred with his black gaze as she lay beneath him, semi-naked and boiling with anger. 'So you know what you can do with your threats of doom and ruin—the same thing you can do with your demands that I play Lelie with you, here in this bed!'

Jared was silent for a long time, his body tensing with every word she spoke, and she could feel the anger emanating from him, feel it tightening his neck muscles, his back, all the way down his spine to the taut muscles

of buttocks, thighs, and round to throb agonisingly in
his rigid manhood.

'Does that make you hate me more?' she whispered,
suddenly aroused again in spite of herself, unable to stop
the *frisson* of terrible excitement burning through her
body. 'Does it, Jared? And does it make you want to
have me even more?'

'Shut up...' he said thickly, but his body pressed deeply
against hers, deep between her splayed, jean-clad thighs.
'You little bitch...'

'You have to learn,' she said huskily, running her
hands down his rigid, locked spine to the tight, hard
buttocks below, squeezing them and shivering with excitement as she heard his fierce groan of agonised need,
'that you want me even more when I defy you!'

'Touch me!' he said hoarsely, fumbling with the zip
of his jeans. 'I can't take any more of this...'

'You'll have to take it, Jared!' Her hand flew to his,
stopping him from unzipping the jeans which were
straining with the pressure of his desire. 'Just as I've had
to take your insults, your hatred, your mistrust and your
threats!'

He started to kiss her throat fiercely, his body moving
against her with insistent pressure.

'That won't work, either!' she whispered. 'You know
as well as I do that I want you! But you have to accept
that I'm your equal! You can't take power over me,
Jared. Not unless you want to wreck any hope of a relationship with me.'

'I don't want a relationship with you!' he said thickly
against her naked, hot throat. 'I just want revenge!'

'Then we'll never reach a compromise.' Tears were
stinging her eyes, but she wasn't going to give in, no
matter how aroused he made her feel, no matter how
much she yearned to feel the release of his body, kept
imagining it, knowing how wildly he would buck and

writhe in the agony of his release if she let him make love to her. It excited and moved her beyond words, but not beyond endurance. She was determined to fight for his respect, even if she had to relinquish his love.

'You don't want a relationship with me either, if you're honest,' he said, kissing her throat hungrily.

'Yes, I do, Jared.'

He tensed even further, then lifted his dark head, staring down at her in stunned silence.

Christie flushed to her hairline. It was difficult to meet his eyes. She knew what she had said was a gamble, and it wasn't one she was prepared to take to double or quits by saying, I love you. But it was a first step—and it was one she had to take, because he quite obviously wasn't ever going to go near it.

'That's why I won't let you take power over me,' she whispered as he stared. 'Why I wouldn't let you do it three years ago, either. Because all I ever wanted from you was equality. An equal relationship, Jared; not a power struggle.'

He looked stricken for a second, then his eyes hardened and he gave a cynical smile. 'Sure. I suppose that's why you're rolling around on a bed, bargaining with me, while your fiancé kicks his heels outside?'

It was on the tip of her tongue to say, The engagement's off. Then she remembered Simon's plea with her not to tell anyone. The words died unspoken, leaving her defenceless and silent. How could she possibly tell Jared that her engagement was over? He would undoubtedly tell Nessa Vale, and then Simon would be humiliated.

'No quick reply for that one?' Jared laughed openly at her. 'I can't say I'm surprised. I didn't let myself hope that you might have a shred of decency left. In fact, I take it all back, Chris. You *are* tough enough for

Hollywood. I wouldn't be surprised to find that you were capable of corrupting even Tinsel-Town itself!'

Anger flared in her. 'I could say the same about you! Or have you forgotten that you're supposed to be Nessa Vale's boyfriend? I wonder how she would feel if she knew what you were trying to do with me!'

'You just let me deal with Nessa.'

'Oh, yes, of course!' She was white with jealousy and pain. 'I might have known your chauvinistic double standards would explain it all away! You can do whatever you want—but women have to just shut up and do as they're told!'

'I wish to God you would!' he bit out thickly.

'Well, that's your tough luck! I'm not going to give in over this, so why don't you just give up?'

'All right!' His dark eyes blazed angrily at her. 'If you won't agree to my terms, I'll have to match your devious little strategies and find a way to *force* you to capitulate!'

She stared, breathless at the threat and the force of his determination to have her. Then she heard herself whisper, 'There is no way...'

'There is, and I'll find it!' He wrenched himself off her, getting off the bed, reaching for his black T-shirt and shouldering into it while she watched, her eyes tracing that magnificence of his bare, bronzed chest while her mind raced at full speed. 'If you think I'm letting you get away with what you've done to me,' he said bitingly as he tucked the T-shirt into his faded jeans, 'you're seriously mistaken.'

Sitting up, she pulled the duvet up to cover her bare breasts. 'But I didn't do anything to you!'

'You used and manipulated and humiliated me!' his hard mouth bit out. 'Now it's my turn. Nobody does that to me—least of all a woman—without getting it all back, with interest!'

'Jared, I loved you,' she said huskily, feeling the bitter
sting of tears and blinking them back. 'I didn't even
know who you were when we met. How can you think
I used you?'

'Say what you want. It makes no difference. I know
what you did, and I know what I'm going to do to get
back at you.'

'Jared, please——'

'I fell in love with you!' he said hoarsely, and strode
back to the bed, eyes blazing with such fury that she
gasped and tried to back away on her knees on the bed,
clutching the duvet to her, but he took her shoulder in
such a fierce grip that she dropped the duvet, kneeling
before him as he towered over her in passionate rage. 'I
loved your beauty, your brains, your smile, your tenderness ... I loved watching you cook for me, iron my
shirts ... I loved it when you listened to me talk about
my childhood, and stroked my hair, held my head against
your breast ...'

'Darling ...' Her voice broke with emotion.

'I loved you when you dressed up and seduced me ...'
he whispered. 'I loved you when you let me dominate
you in bed ... I loved you when you talked about our
children ...' His hands bit into her bare shoulders. 'And
when you left me, when you threw all that away, I had
to stand back and watch you soar into the Hollywood
sky like a comet ... and I realised I loved something else
about you, something that was there all the time, something I'd loved without ever recognising it.'

His face blurred before her eyes.

'Your talent!' he said thickly. 'I loved your talent.'

She groped for his shoulders, blind with tears of love.

'And now I'm going to use it against you,' he whispered fiercely. 'It's poetic justice—don't you see that?
You used your talent to convince me you loved me.'

'No ...' She could hardly see, hardly speak.

'Now I'm going to use it to get my revenge.' He stared down at her for a second, then his long hand snaked into her hair, tangled in it, pulled her head slowly but surely back.

'Oh...' she gasped in pain.

'No need to act any more, my darling!' His other hand stroked her bare breast as she knelt on the bed at his mercy. 'You'll be able to just be yourself with me!' He bent his dark head, his mouth closed over hers, and his kiss was passionate, making her moan in abject desire, and making him give a rough exclamation of excitement as he whispered, 'Oh, you want it just as much as I do! Say you'll do it now! Give us both what we need so badly!'

'Never!' she whispered against his hot mouth. 'I'll never let you do that to me. I'll never give in, and I'll never go on the casting couch with you!'

His hand jerked her hair angrily, then released her with a faint shove. 'It's going to be a fight, then, is it?' He stepped back from the bed, face hard. 'Very well. But I warn you, Chris, I'll win it in the end—no matter what it takes.' Turning on his heel, he strode to the door. 'Even if I have to ruin your career to do it! You will dance to my tune, Christie McCall! I can promise you that!'

Christie stared after him, tears slipping hotly over her lashes, blinding her as the door slammed, and she found herself collapsing on the bed to cry until her heart nearly broke.

Talk about losing the biggest gamble of her life! Oh, God, the pain just went on and on, smashing her dreams to pieces everywhere she looked, leaving her feeling as though she had walked over broken glass for nothing.

He hated her so bitterly. How could she ever fight that hatred and win? He was never going to forgive her for what he believed she had done to him, and he was never going to accept that he was wrong about her.

Damn those stupid articles about her! Christie covered her hot face with her hands, rolling into a little ball and crying even harder. It must have something to do with them that Jared refused to let go of his opinion of her. When she left him for fame, he had hardened his heart to her, but when those articles had come out his heart had simply slammed shut to her forever, and nothing she could do would open it again.

Not only had she lost her love—she had risked her whole career.

And for what?

She sobbed deeply, raging as she cried, hating everything now, the whole world turning black as despair closed in on her and she questioned her entire life. All this work, for such a bitter reward. She thought of drama school, the fun of it, the endless grind of voice lessons, acting lessons, fencing lessons . . . the excitement of rehearsals, the end-of-term shows. How wonderful it had all seemed to her then! And how the movie world had glittered enticingly beyond theatre, beckoning her on as she dreamed and dreamed of becoming like one of her idols. Was this how it ended up for them? she wondered in despair. With the casting couch? The lies, the corruption and the callous way people bartered with love and human souls, just in order to get that picture made the way they wanted, just to make the rest of the world see them as the false icons they were?

A Jared Buchanan picture, she thought savagely, tears streaming down her face. What a tragedy he was! How could he have come here and broken her heart like this, her faith in love.

Yet he had been so convincing . . .

The light came back as she remembered his hoarse voice, the pain blazing in his eyes as he said, 'I fell in love with your talent and now I'm going to use it against you!' Her eyes welled up again with tears of a different sort as anger faded and hope took its place, leaving her swinging wildly back to belief in him, faith in him, and trust filtering back as the darkness fell away.

Had he really lied? She couldn't believe it! Oh, he had sounded so real, so loving, and so like the man she had fallen in love with all those years ago. Jared Buchanan: a passionate, obsessive, emotional man who prized talent beyond rubies in his professional life.

Was it possible that what Jared was really fighting against was love?

Sitting up, she dashed her tears away and struggled to think. It was so hard to be objective when your whole life was on the line. But she had to try, even though she was still on the edge of losing her love, her man, her future happiness and her career.

If he loved her talent, he must love her. He couldn't possibly list all those qualities he had loved in her without still feeling something other than hatred and contempt.

And if he did feel love beneath his hatred, then he must be going through the same kind of hell as her right now.

Only Jared could answer that. But dared she approach him again? No, she didn't dare, and she knew it. The thought of putting her heart on the line again for him was enough to send her screaming out of this white palace by the sea, and running all the way back to Beverly Hills in her bare feet.

But she *had* to know if she was right—that Jared loved her and had meant every word he said when he listed every quality he had ever loved in her, including her talent.

She'd have to be brave.

She'd have to confront him.

Getting off the bed, she didn't allow herself to think about what she was doing, she just pulled on her bra and then her lace top, buttoning it with shaky fingers. A glance in the mirror showed raw red eyes swollen from crying. She looked like a tragic Chekhov heroine.

To hell with what I look like, she thought fiercely, it's time I stopped worrying about anything other than making Jared see, really see, that I love him, that I'm not what he thinks I am, and that he's got to stop hating me.

Determined, she went downstairs.

Lunch was being served by the pool. It was one o'clock, the sun was like a gold furnace, and music played lightly from a radio as waiters moved around the tables with vast silver tureens of Caesar salad.

'Oh, my lord!' drawled Millie, staring at Christie as she emerged from the house. 'What happened to her?'

Jared, standing by the drinks table with Mike, turned his head to look at her. He was wearing dark glasses. She met his gaze, lifting her head, not hiding the bruised expression in her eyes, nor the tremor of her mouth as she felt herself more vulnerable than she had ever been.

Without allowing herself to collapse with fright, she marched straight over to him, watched by the others in breathless anticipation of another love scene played in public.

'I want to speak to you privately, please,' she said in an unsteady voice as soon as she reached Jared.

Jared's eyes narrowed sharply.

'Immediately, please,' Christie said.

Mike grinned at her, then at Jared. Everyone was watching with bated breath. Jared had no option other than to give a cool, hard smile and say politely, 'Of course. Shall we go into the house?'

'No.' She didn't want to be alone with him where he could either kiss or insult her angrily. 'Out here will do.'

Glancing around, she pointed to the pool. 'Over there. OK?'

'OK.' He put his drink down, gave Mike a curt nod, and strode coolly with Christie across the terrace to the glittering blue pool.

It was almost an inner sanctum. The Roman statues surrounded them, rich green grass beyond the sun-bleached patio, and nobody could hear what they said there, they were alone with the impassive white statues.

'You're going to tell me you've decided to take the role of——'

'No,' Christie said huskily, and stopped walking, aware they were out of earshot now, and ready to risk everything on this one, final confrontation. 'This has nothing to do with fame, fortune or films, Jared. I want to talk to you about us.'

He stopped too, towering over her, his smile cynical. 'You've decided to accept my terms for——'

'Jared,' she cut in, looking away from him, her heart pounding with nerves, 'do you remember when we first met?'

He gave a hard smile. 'How could I forget!'

'I thought you were just a handsome cameraman,' she said, ignoring his cynicism. 'And when I found out you were a world-famous director, I tried to get out of our dinner date. So you said to me, Can't you just pretend I'm a cameraman? Treat me as though I really am what you thought I was before?'

'Yes, I remember,' he said tersely. 'What of it?'

'Well...' She looked up at him, and the warm breeze lifted strands of her blonde hair back from her tear-ravaged face. 'Can you do that with me? Just for the next five minutes? Pretend I'm the woman you fell in love with—and forget that you think I'm like Lelie?'

He gave a harsh laugh. 'Why should I do that?'

'Because I have a few things to tell you,' she said bravely. 'And I just can't face telling you them when you keep insulting me, hurting me, and talking about revenge.'

Jared's eyes narrowed. 'What is this!'

'My last attempt to make you listen to me.' Her eyes glittered in the hot sunlight. 'I've tried everything I can think of, and now I'm just going to put my cards on the table, but I can't do it if you keep treating me like an enemy.'

'Too bad!' he drawled. 'It's how I see you.'

'Well, I need you to see me as the woman you loved!' she said fiercely. 'Now, come on, Jared! I did it for you three years ago! You can do it for me now! Just for five minutes—is that so much to ask? Or have you forgotten how important it was to you back then? It's as important to me now, and I need you to do it!'

He stared at her in silence for a moment, and behind the dark glasses his eyes were fierce with emotion.

'I went ahead with that date, Jared. Even though I felt frightened and inferior, I sat with you all night and pretended you were just my handsome cameraman. And then I——' She was trembling with nerves, but still brave. 'I fell in love with you, in spite of my feelings of inadequacy. I let you into my life, let you take my virginity, make love to me—I was ready to marry you, too, even though I did genuinely feel inferior. If I could do all of that for you—why can't you just pretend none of this has happened? Pretend I'm still the woman you loved and trusted? Just for five minutes?'

He was pale beneath his tan, the skin stretched tautly over his hard bones. For a second she thought he'd refuse, because of the tough line of his mouth.

Then he gave a terse nod, glanced at his watch, and said thickly, 'Five minutes!'

Christie almost collapsed with relief, but she knew he didn't truly believe yet, not as she had three years ago, so she said huskily, 'Take off your dark glasses. Let me see your eyes.'

His mouth tightened, but he slowly removed them, and she stared deeply into them as the seconds ticked by.

'Your eyes are so clear,' she said softly. 'Mine aren't. I just cried myself into a wreck upstairs. Are you really so unaffected by what's been happening between us, Jared?'

He said nothing, but his gaze moved over her tear-ravaged face.

'I . . .' She touched his arm, smiling. 'I'm going to ask you something, Jared, and if you're to keep your side of this particular bargain, you will answer me honestly.' She drew a level breath. 'Is your hatred of me based on my involvement with Simon? I mean—I know the articles didn't help, and the way we split up was disastrous, but— is Simon one of the major reasons you believe I'm like Lelie?'

'You must know it is!' he said tightly.

'Then I want to tell you the truth about Simon. But you must swear to me that you won't tell anyone else.' Her fingers tightened on his arm. 'Swear it, Jared! I know you'll keep your word if you give it.'

'All right,' he said, eyes narrowing. 'You have my word that I won't repeat a word of this conversation to anyone.'

She drew a level breath, then said, 'I came out here with Simon three years ago as actress and agent. For the first two and a half years, that's how we remained. But we got lonely, Jared. That's all. Two old friends who couldn't bear to face the emotional desert they had built for themselves on the altar of ambition.'

Jared looked away, his face hard. 'Touching!'

'So...' she struggled to ignore his blatant disbelief '...we just kind of got together. There's no real passion or mad desire. We're just friends, trying not to be lonely. And I thought it would work—we both did. Until we came here, to Casa Camarra.'

He gave a rough laugh. 'I suppose you're going to say that you've now realised it isn't going to work, and the reason you have is because you met me again et cetera, et cetera, blah blah blah!' His dark eyes were angry. 'See? I can almost read your mind! But don't let me stop your convincing little act. You just carry on.'

'Don't do this to me!' she burst out furiously, eyes flashing. 'You just gave me your word that you'd believe in me—and my time isn't up yet! I still have three minutes left!'

He looked away again, silent.

'But why am I bothering?' she said bitterly. 'Coming to you like this, trying to get through to you, when it's perfectly obvious I'm just wasting my time!'

'Yes, why are you, Chris?' he said thickly. 'Or shall I guess? You're scared stiff I'm going to get angry enough to try and ruin your career if you keep refusing to——'

'To hell with my career!' she said hoarsely, and he almost flinched in shock. 'I haven't been able to think about it properly since I got here and met you again! I can't believe my whole life could have changed this much, in such a short time, but it has! I knew before I came here that I was ready for marriage, children, settling down, giving up the race, but...' She drew an unsteady breath, shaking her blonde head, staring at him. 'My God, I didn't expect all this to happen!

'I've lived my whole life under the pressure of needing fame. I always knew that once I'd achieved it, I'd be able to relax, lie back and live; just live. Get married, have children, stop running in the rat race...' She looked up suddenly into his eyes. 'And you know what I'm talking about, don't you? It's what you wanted, when we first met. My God, Jared . . . you'd already reached the point in your life that I'm reaching now.'

'I . . .' He broke off abruptly, angrily, snarling, 'Why the hell am I listening to all of this!'

'That's why you were ready to get married and have children.' She felt her eyes sting without warning as tears welled up and she began to understand what was really happening to her. 'But I wasn't ready, Jared, because I wasn't famous, and I just couldn't relax until I was.'

'I don't want to hear any——'

'But I'm ready now.' The tears spilled out over her lashes.

'Oh, God——'

'Jared, you must believe me!'

'I don't want to hear this!' he said roughly. 'And I don't want to see your tears, damn it!' He stared, then grabbed her shoulders, saying fiercely, 'Stop crying! Stop it!'

'I can't!' The tears were streaming down her face: 'You've been so vile to me, so full of hate and hardness——'

'What the hell do you want from me?' he bit out thickly. 'I mean—what do you want me to say?'

'You must still feel something for me!' she whispered. 'I've told you what Simon means to me! I need to know what Nessa means to you!'

'She's an old friend. Don't ask for any more than that, because I damned well won't tell you!'

'And me? Who am I to you?'

He stared down into her eyes, emotion blazing between them as she gripped his chest. He held her shoulders, and the tears streamed down her face.

'I feel a lot of things for you,' he said roughly. 'Mostly hatred and contempt. But they're mingled with admiration and respect—which only makes me want to hurt you more. I hate knowing you've made it on your own like this. I hate knowing you're better off not being a perfect wife and mother. And I hate knowing that I respect you for it.'

Her heart was skipping wildly. 'Jared, I——'

'How can I feel respect for a woman like you?' he bit out savagely. 'You're dangerous to any man fool enough to care about you! All right, you're talented, beautiful, clever and sexy as hell—but you're not a real woman. If and when you ever show love or tenderness, it's only as a means to an end. You manipulate, lie, cheat and scheme the way most women just plain love and understand their men. And don't give me that devastated look! It won't work any more than your phoney tears! I've watched you on screen, remember, as well as in real life, and I *know* you're just using your talent to make me feel sorry for you!' His mouth twisted with fury. 'Well, it won't work, Chris! I've told you the score—I hate your guts, I want revenge, and I'm going to use your talent against you! Now have you got that? Is that plain enough for you? Or shall I write it on a billboard ten miles high so the whole of Hollywood can see it?'

Struck dumb by the force of his hatred, and the reality of her abject failure to get through to him, she could only stand and stare at him, white with pain, as the tears flowed silently over her cheeks.

'Good,' Jared said thickly, releasing her. 'Maybe now you'll come to terms with what you're going to have to do to placate my very justifiable anger.' Without another word, he turned on his heel and strode away from her.

She wanted to reach out and call him back, but of course she knew she would be humiliated if she did. He wasn't going to change his mind. He wasn't going to believe her. Not if he lived to be a hundred, he would never, never allow himself to believe that he could have been wrong about her and that they could have a love worth saving.

At least I tried, she told herself. At least I came down here, told him the truth, tried to get the truth out of him, and stopped trying to hide how much I loved him.

Yes, and just look where it got me. Tears stung her eyes again. She couldn't cope any more. Endless crying, endless pain, endless battles. Sinking down on the hot stone patio, she kicked off her sandals, rolled up her jeans and let her feet slide into the cool water of the pool.

Here, at least, she could cry in private. So long as she just sat here and did nothing, no one would notice that tears were still slipping down her golden cheeks.

She felt as though this weekend had taken her and smashed her repeatedly against a brick wall until she was only just able to stand, but no longer knew how or why or where, because every fixed point on the map was obliterated.

Her engagement was off, her career in jeopardy, and her heart in little tiny pieces on the floor.

A shadow fell over her beside the pool.

'Hi.' Simon's eyes were gentle. 'Are you all right?'

'Not really,' she confessed huskily. 'You'd better sit down, though. I'm afraid I just told Jared that we were only friends, nothing more passionate or long-lasting than that.'

Simon sighed and sank down beside her on the edge of the hot pool. 'Don't worry. I told Nessa the same thing about you.'

She laughed, and they sat together in companionable silence for a few calm, tranquil minutes.

'Simon,' she said eventually, 'is there any way we can just leave this wretched place? Just pack our bags and go back to Beverly Hills?'

'I wish to God there were,' he said, just as miserable. 'But it would ruin our relationship with Camarra Pictures.'

She sighed heavily. 'You're right. I just feel right now that there's no way I can stand to stay...'

'Don't worry——' he gave a pained smile '—there's only another twenty-four hours of hell to get through. This time tomorrow we'll all be packing our cases and getting ready to leave.'

A curious mixture of pain and disappointment touched her heart. 'Yes...'

'And Millie will keep us busy until then,' he pointed out. 'She's organised a treasure hunt through the grounds this afternoon, and then there's the Camarra Ball to-night. So by the time we've got through all that lot, it'll be almost time to leave.'

'Almost time to leave...' she murmured huskily, and felt like crying her eyes out again. Would she ever see Jared again? Or would he try to hunt her down, determined to get his revenge. No matter what he said, she knew she wouldn't give it to him, so he would have no choice but to eventually give up the quest.

That made her want to cry again. How could she be such a fool? It was as though she'd rather see Jared, be with him, argue with him—than simply go away and start a new life somewhere else.

Because I know I'll never fall in love with anyone else again, she realised with a dull shock. There is no other man I could love. No one else has his qualities, his powerful attraction, or his talent.

The tears were welling up again behind her dark glasses.

All this crying—she must surely have cleansed her heart of love by now?

CHAPTER NINE

MILLIE'S treasure hunt was an excellent way to spend the afternoon. They were all given question sheets with clues, and the first team to get all the answers had to go to the hallway to collect the prize—a little marble model of Casa Camarra itself, with the date of their visit engraved in jade. Very few people had these little models of Casa Camarra, and although both Christie and Simon were deeply preoccupied with their own love-lives, they both wanted to win, and it did help take their minds off their problems, just a little.

'Jared and Nessa have teamed up, too,' Simon said thickly, as they all collected their question sheets from Millie. 'I hope they don't win, or Nessa will really rub my nose in it. She's already got a Casa Camarra model for winning seven years ago.'

Christie was still amazed by how long he and Nessa had known each other. Her eyes jealously stared at Nessa standing with Jared, and it occurred to her suddenly that they were more equals than she and Jared. That made her jealousy run riot like an injection of pure poison.

'Come on.' Simon nudged her. 'We'll get left behind if we don't start off now...'

The treasure hunt took them through the grounds with questions like: Where might Cecil B. DeMille and Hieronymous Bosch find a love of epics in common? They found a little walled garden with a brass plaque on the gates saying, 'Earthly Delights'. Simon scribbled the answer down while Christie stared through the gates

139

at the beautiful sunlit garden, and felt shut out from paradise because Jared did not love her.

When they got back to the house, it was deserted.

The sun beat down on the bleached stone balconies, terrace and palm trees. Music was playing from an upstairs window, a lively modern love song that was last year's number one on the billboard charts.

Suddenly, Jared stepped out on to a balcony on the east wing.

'Oh, my God!' Simon went white, his voice pained as he stopped dead, staring up at the sun-drenched balcony. 'That's her room! He's with Nessa, in her bed——'

Nessa wafted out on to the balcony then, beautiful in a white towelling robe and obviously naked beneath it, leaning on the stone railing next to Jared, both their backs to the gardens, their laughter lilting softly above the music.

They kissed briefly, gently, tenderly.

'I can't stand it!' Christie said in a hoarse whisper, turning to Simon, groping blindly for his arms. 'Get me out of here, get me away from this place!'

His arms shot around her, holding her close as he gave a rough groan of despair. 'We can't leave, Christie! We'll have to put on a brave face and——'

'I haven't got a brave face any more!' She buried her face in his neck, clinging to him. 'Not after this! They've been making love—haven't they? Look at her! She's obviously naked under that——'

'Don't, don't!' Simon bit out shakingly, burying his face in her hair. 'Don't say it, I don't want to hear it, don't want to think about it!'

She drew back, tears in her eyes. 'You're right! There's no point in torturing ourselves.' Blindly, she groped for his hand. 'Come on—let's go and report to Millie with our answers. There's only a short while left of this nightmare, and then we can go home.'

In the hall, Mike and Millie lounged on the red-carpeted stairs, drinking piña coladas while Valentino watched them with brooding black-rimmed eyes, looking as though he was dying of thirst in the desert and could just do with a sip of their drinks.

'Are we the last to arrive?' Simon clipped out with a bright, false smile that hid his pain over Nessa.

'No, you're the first,' Mike drawled, beckoning with a stubby hand. 'Here—let's see the quiz sheets, make sure you've done it properly.'

Christie watched Simon take him the piece of paper, and felt the bitter irony burn into her heart. She had lost everything. Her faith, her love, her dreams, her role in the film. It had all happened here in Casa Camarra on one brief weekend. And now, in a final act of mockery, she had won a coveted marble model of the wretched white palace by the sea complete with finely sculpted jade palm trees, to commemmorate the whole affair.

'Yep.' Mike clicked his pen. 'You're the winners. Who wants the model?'

'Give it to Christie,' Simon said thickly.

Mike got to his feet and strode with his arrogant swagger to her. 'Here you are, Miss McCall!' He handed her the beautiful model and kissed her with lips that tasted of cigars and sweet coconut alcohol. 'Casa Camarra. Congratulations. That'll be worth some money in a few years' time.'

'I heard,' said Millie, 'that a 1927 model sold for almost a million dollars last month.'

'This is where you have your name inscribed.' Mike pointed to a small twenty-four-carat gold plaque to the right of the tiny front doors.

'It's beautiful,' Christie said unsteadily, trying to smile. 'I'll take great care of it. It will always remind me of this weekend.'

Simon winced and ran an elegant hand through his hair. 'Is there anything else on the agenda for this afternoon? Or just cruising to the party tonight?'

'No, you've got the afternoon free from now.' Millie sighed. 'It's four-thirty already, so you can't do much with it. Don't forget to wear your most glamorous clothes for the Ball, though.'

'Yes, we've got a lot of people coming,' Mike agreed, grey brows lifting. 'Two hundred of the most important people in Hollywood. So do Camarra Pictures proud, honey.' He patted Christie's shoulder and winked at her. 'Look like our brightest young star...'

Later, in her room, she sat staring at the beautiful model of Casa Camarra, wondering how she would feel in twenty years' time when she saw it on her mantelpiece, gathering dust. What would her life be like then? She probably wouldn't be married, or have any children. She would probably be a great star, world famous and completely alone.

Suddenly, none of it seemed worth it. What point was there in being famous and successful and unloved? Oh, there would always be other men who would attract her, maybe even propose to her. But she knew she would be lucky to find another man she could love as much as she had loved Jared Buchanan.

And I must stop loving him immediately, she thought in despair, because he clearly doesn't love me. How could he have gone to bed with Nessa this afternoon, almost straight after hearing Christie's emotional plea? It was worse than a betrayal; it was actually distasteful, and she knew she could never forgive him for it, nor for drawing her into this emotional nightmare she had been subjected to this weekend.

They could just have had a civilised, if painful, working relationship on *Tigresse*. But no, Jared wouldn't

let that be, he had to make those despicable demands
about the casting couch, and force her to reject the role.

But what was the point of thinking about it? She was
only destroying herself by sitting here, staring at that
beautiful, delicate model of Casa Camarra and dwelling
on the emotional traumas that her weekend here had
inflicted on her.

It was five-thirty now, and time she started getting
ready for the Camarra Ball. All of Hollywood would be
there, and their glamour would be out in force for this,
the most spectacular of occasions. Christie would go up
a dozen notches in everybody's estimation once they
discovered that she was one of the lucky dozen people
to be a weekend guest at the biannual Camarra Ball.

She had drawn a strike against herself by rejecting the
role of Tigresse. Tonight was a chance to try and make
up for that in Mike's eyes, by looking as glamorous as
possible.

Going in the bathroom, she ran a bath, poured a little
Obsession oil into it, and undressed amid the scented
steam. Then she lolled in it broodingly, thinking of Jared,
until the scented water was lukewarm. She washed her
long blonde hair, conditioned it, then rinsed it until it
was squeaky clean, performing mundane beauty rituals
as though in a trance.

She wondered what Nessa Vale was doing to make
herself beautiful. Was she making love with Jared again?
Her heart skidded away from the thought in desperation, but it was no use, it crashed into the reality of
their love affair because the memory of that moment on
the balcony was forever burnt into her mind. No telling
herself it might be a platonic relationship any more, or
telling herself Jared couldn't be in love with Nessa because he spent so much time with Christie.

The plain truth had been revealed this afternoon as
they laughed and kissed on the balcony, lovers for all

the world to see while that breathy, catchy love song
played in the hot afternoon warmth.

It was easy to choose the right dress for tonight.

The white-blue satin full-length dress had a plunging
sweetheart neckline, tiny shoulder straps, a tight, fitted
waist and even more tightly fitted hips, sliding down to
the floor with a long slit up the front of one thigh.

It looked breathtakingly sexy and elegant at the same
time. The diamond choker sparkled around her slender
throat as she pulled long evening gloves on, and her
blonde hair cascaded around her beautiful face like spun
silk.

What a movie-star, she thought bitterly.

What a life's work.

It was seven-thirty, and the house was filled with music
and activity as the band began playing in the ballroom,
servants put the finishing touches to the vast buffet and
waiters began popping champagne corks on vintage
Bollinger to pour into cascading pyramids of glasses.

Cars were arriving, great fleets of Cadillacs, Rolls-
Royces, Ferraris and limousine after limousine, sweeping
up that hot, dusty drive to Casa Camarra as everyone
came to the white palace by the sea, eager to be part of
the glittering, glamorous élite.

The knock on her door made her heart soar with hope,
foolish hope, that it might be Jared come to tell her
something, anything, that would explain what she had
seen this afternoon, what he had said this morning, and
tell her that he loved her truly...

'Christie...?' Simon opened the door. Her hope died.

'Hi.' She managed a smile.

He smiled. 'You look like the cat's miaow in that dress,
darling! I've never seen you so stunning!'

'Thanks.' Pain shone in her eyes as they moved over
his elegant grey Ralph Lauren suit. 'You look very
handsome yourself.'

He smiled and held out his hand, because they had to arrive together, of course. They were the only protection they had against the nightmare of facing Jared and Nessa after seeing that there was no longer any doubt: they really were lovers.

'Remember when we arrived here yesterday?' Simon said as they walked down the sweeping staircase together.

'Was it really only yesterday?'

'And I said we'd made it.' He laughed bitterly. 'Right to the top of the heap, I said, didn't I?'

Her eyes met Vivien Leigh's. 'Right to the top...'

'I can't help feeling this has all been hubris.' He gave her a bitter smile as they passed Jean Harlow. 'I rather tempted the gods, didn't I, in my arrogance?'

'It's very difficult not to,' she pointed out with a sympathetic smile, 'when you get the rewards for hard work. And you have worked hard, Simon. We both have. I suppose it's just that there is truth in the old saying— lucky at cards, unlucky in love.'

'Yes.' They were in the hall now, and music was everywhere, echoing along the marble walls and pillars where the immortals of Hollywood looked down on yet another year, yet another weekend party, yet another ball at the palace by the sea.

They rounded the sweeping white corner, and the ballroom was at the end of the black-white corridor, great gold doors flung open, music getting louder, more beautiful.

'I'm going to confront Jared,' Christie heard herself say without warning as they walked hand in hand towards the music and the dancing and the voices. She laughed at her own sudden bravery. 'Yes! I'm going to confront him about seeing him with Nessa.' She laughed again, courage flowing through her veins as she finally let go of the hope she had nursed all along that he might love her, and accepted his vile character for what it was, leaving her free to confront him. 'I'm going to tell him exactly what I think of him!'

Simon laughed softly and shot her a look of admiration. 'Good for you. Shall I slap Nessa around the face with it, too?'

Angry pain leapt in her eyes and heart. 'Why not? She's done her best to hurt you this weekend, just as Jared has me. For all we know they're both in it together and laughing at us behind our backs. Nothing would surprise me about Tinsel-Town any more—or the people who run it!'

'Me neither,' he laughed angrily. 'But at least I've always protected you from the casting couch.'

Rage flooded her veins as they entered the ballroom, and flashbulbs exploded in her face, making her pose immediately, one hand on Simon's elegant shoulder, smiling as best she could, the glitter of pain and anger in her blue eyes only enhancing her beauty photographically.

'Stunning!' Mike Camarra drawled, striding over, cigar in mouth, and giving her a bear hug. 'Knew you wouldn't let me down, Christie! Have a glass of champagne, and go mingle with the guests!'

Clutching her champagne, she looked around the glittering, packed ballroom, with its cavernous ceiling, marble pillars, mirrored walls, potted palms in sleek white pots, and the band playing in full evening dress on the stage at the far end, way beyond the heads of the rich, famous and beautiful guests.

Jared and Nessa were dancing. Jealousy savaged her as she watched Nessa smiling up at him, her body so close to his as they moved to the music that they were practically making love.

God, she felt such a fool! The whole time she'd been here, she'd believed almost everything he said, discounted Nessa's presence right up until the last minute, so convinced that he couldn't feel more for Nessa than he did for her, just because he was chasing her so intently...

'Dance with me!' Simon said thickly beside her.

She put her champagne down on a passing silver tray. Together, she and Simon moved on to the dance-floor, dancing as close together as Jared and Nessa.

'I feel as though I'm being mauled by a pack of savage dogs,' Simon said painfully, staring over Christie's slender shoulder at Nessa.

'Me too,' she whispered. 'But you mustn't let her see how badly she's affecting you.'

They danced another three dances, then could stand it no longer, mutually agreeing to stop putting up such a terrible show when they were dying inside.

Moving over to the tables groaning under the weight of food, they stared without interest at the fresh lobster, roast beef, roast suckling pig glazed in honey, and the caviar, the quail's eggs, the delicacies from all over the world.

Christie sighed at the sight of the food, and glanced round.

'Don't look!' Simon bit out. 'He's kissing her!'

Her heart winced as though stabbed. She stared, mesmerised by savage jealousy as Jared bent his dark head to kiss that smiling red mouth.

'Have some caviar!' Mike Camarra was suddenly beside them, clapping Simon on the back and extending a silver pot to him. 'Finest Beluga! Here—you, too, Christie!'

Turning back to him, she was forced, as Simon was, to stand talking to him, admiring his Beluga caviar.

'Not fattening, either.' Millie joined them, laughing in approval as Christie ate little bites of caviar. 'That's the wonder of it.'

'Simon doesn't have to worry about his figure, though.' Mike Camarra liked people who ate with him. 'Here, Simon—join me in a large helping of everything on this table!'

'You pig!' Millie laughed, very drunk on Bollinger.

'Roast suckling pig, honey!' Mike cracked, piling two plates high with food while Simon watched him, aghast.

Millie turned to Christie. 'Enjoying the weekend, honey?'

'Yes, it's been wonderful,' she lied politely. 'And it was very generous of you to invite us.'

'Yes...pity about the way things are turning out.' Millie took another glass of champagne from a passing tray. 'I really wanted Simon and Nessa to get back together. They were made for each other, you know.'

Christie stared at her in horror, then at Simon, who was listening, grey eyes blazing with ill-concealed fury.

'Eat up.' Mike jogged Simon's frozen arm.

'He belonged with Nessa,' Millie ranted on. 'They were stupid, both of them, to ever consider breaking up. And don't look furious, honey; you quite obviously belonged with Jared Buchanan.'

In horror, she suddenly saw Jared and Nessa making a beeline for them, hand in hand, her red lipstick on his hard, handsome cheek, both looking stunning, Jared in a frighteningly expensive black Armani suit, and Nessa the perfect foil in a blood-red silk clinging number.

'Ah, here comes Jared now!' Millie laughed, drinking more. 'What he's doing with Nessa when he could have you, I'll never know. Nessa's not right for him. It's you he wants.'

'Millie——' she broke out shakingly.

'Stands out a mile, the way you two look at each other. All that brooding passion! And as for you suddenly refusing to play Lelie, right out of the blue, well—it's plain as cherry-pie that you did it because you were still in love with Jared.'

Jared and Nessa were beside them suddenly, catching the tail end of that, both staring at Millie in shock.

'Well, well, well!' drawled Millie, sipping champagne, eyes glittering. 'The party's really hotting up!'

'You really are a nasty piece of work,' Jared bit out under his breath, eyes raking his hostess with contempt. 'If it weren't for the high esteem in which I hold your husband, I'd be tempted to call you a string of very unrepeatable names!'

Millie flushed angrily. 'Mike!' She turned. 'Did you hear that, Mike!'

'Sure I did, honey!' Mike drawled right behind her, eating a large chicken leg. 'And I'm not impressed. But you can't blame the man. We are interfering like mad, and you know it.'

'I agree,' Simon said through a mouthful of garlic sausage. 'And I think I've had just about enough of it!' He angrily threw his plate down on the table, taking a step towards Millie, bristling with rage. 'Much as I detest Jared for my own personal reasons, I must agree with him. You are a thoroughly poisonous woman, and richly deserve to be called a string of unrepeatable names.'

'Shut up, Simon!' Nessa hissed, trembling. 'They'll blacklist you, you fool!'

He turned to her, eyes blazing, and bit out, 'Keep out of this, you bloody bitch!'

Nessa went scarlet with rage. 'You dare call me a bitch! In public! After the way you've behaved!'

'The way I've behaved!' Simon grabbed her arm, shouting hoarsely, 'You cheap little tramp! I saw you on the balcony today! I know you'd been to bed with that swine all afternoon!'

'You lying little reptile!' Jared bit out, bristling with aggression. 'If anyone's been playing with two women, it's you!'

Christie stepped forwards. 'Don't try to pin this on Simon! He's suffered enough because of you!'

'You stay out of it!' Jared snarled, whirling on her. 'I saw your passionate embrace with him, right beneath the balcony!'

'What?'

'And to think I actually believed what you said to me this afternoon!' Jared hurled, completely losing his temper now. 'My God, I really asked for a slug in the guts, didn't I, looking out of the balcony to see you behaving like the double-dealing little cheat you are!'

Simon pushed at him furiously. 'Don't talk to her like that, you swine!'

'You're going the right way to get a punch in the mouth!' Jared moved towards him menacingly, bristling with aggression, ready to fight. 'I've wanted to knock your face through the back of your head for years now, and——'

'Go ahead!' Simon shouted miserably, backing away. 'What do I care! You've stolen the only woman I loved and now I've got nothing to live for! Nothing but——'

'You never loved me!' Nessa said fiercely. 'Don't try to pull that old trick on me, because I won't believe it!'

'I don't care if you—I don't care if——' he broke off suddenly, a peculiar expression in his eyes.

There was a split-second's silence.

'Ah...!' Simon clutched at his chest, going white, staggering.

Jared went white, too. 'Oh, my God!'

'My heart...'

Everyone just stared at him in shocked realisation.

'Get back!' Jared moved like lightning, catching Simon before he collapsed on to the tables. 'Call an ambulance!'

A hushed gasp fell as Jared laid Simon on the floor, Millie ran to dial emergency, Christie knelt shakingly beside Simon and Jared, and everyone in the ballroom began to close in around them all.

'Stand back, for God's sake!' Jared shouted as the music died away and his hands were deftly loosening Simon's tie, tearing his shirt open. 'Give him some space, he needs to breathe!'

'Nessa...!' Simon whispered with difficulty, holding out a shaking hand.

'I'm here, darling!' Nessa knelt beside him, tears in her eyes as she gripped his hand. 'Try not to talk. I couldn't bear it if anything happened to you!'

'I might die, Ness!' he murmured, his face ashen as he clung to her hand.

'No! Please...'

'If I do,' he said, 'I want you to know the truth.'

She started to weep. 'Oh, Simon...'

'I loved you all along, Ness. Right from the minute I first saw you, crying at your parents' party because you hadn't won the prize for Prettiest Party Dress. Do you remember?'

'I was only three...' Nessa's tears streamed down her cheeks.

'And you should have won Prettiest Party Dress,' he said huskily, 'because it was such a pretty dress you wore that day. Big pink sash around your waist and hundreds of little sausage curls...'

'My mother spent hours doing my hair,' Nessa laughed tearfully. 'And then it all got ruined when you pushed me in the swimming-pool.'

Simon laughed too, then groaned and clutched his chest.

'Try not to excite him,' Jared said grimly. 'It's a long drive for the paramedics.'

'Darling...' Simon was white with pain now, clutching Nessa's hand as she wept unstoppably. 'I wanted you to be such a great star, and I was so sure I'd be known as your Svengali when you made it. But nobody took as much notice of me as I'd thought they would.'

'It wasn't your fault, darling,' she whispered, stroking his white brow. 'It was because we'd grown up together, that's why nobody said you were my Roger Vadim.'

'And I grew so jealous of you,' he confessed, tears sliding over his lashes now and down the side of his temples. 'I can't believe I did what I did. Destroyed us both in front of Hollywood...'

'I loved you,' Nessa cried, 'even when you were doing it!'

'Ness...that affair with Sally Harker. It never happened. I made it all up just to get back at you.'

'Oh, God, no!' Nessa stared at him in horror. 'Oh, Simon, Simon, why didn't you tell me before!'

He winced, clutching his chest, muttering thickly, 'Too proud.'

'Don't let him get worked up!' Jared said tightly, ready to go into action should his heart stop altogether.

'Couldn't admit it,' Simon said, 'not after I came to your apartment that day and found your new agent there. How could I tell you my love affair had been a sham, when you were obviously in a very hot situation with that bastard?'

Nessa moaned, tears wrecking her make-up beyond repair. 'But he wasn't my lover, Simon! He just stayed the night because he was too drunk to drive home!'

'You mean——' Simon stared, his face sheened with sweat now.

'I was pretending as much as you, you fool!' she cried emotionally. 'I still am! All weekend—oh, God, what a nightmare, what a bloody hellish time it's been! Having to smile, and smile and pretend not to care that you're engaged to her, and——'

'What!' Simon's grey eyes stared intently. 'But what about Jared? He's your lover! I saw you on the balcony with——'

'I fell in the swimming pool,' she groaned. 'Fully clothed on the treasure hunt. Talk about childhood patterns!'

'I helped her out,' Jared said deeply, watching Simon for signs of oncoming cardiac arrest, his face very tense. 'We abandoned the treasure hunt and she went up to get changed.'

Christie was staring in disbelief.

So was Simon. 'But you were in her bedroom! You—you kissed her! I saw you, we both saw you!'

Jared nodded. 'We're old friends now. The last three years, we've done nothing but confide in each other about——' He broke off, a dark flush invading his handsome face as he darted a quick, intense look at Christie. 'About our broken hearts.'

'Jared…!' Christie whispered breathlessly. 'Oh, Jared, darling!'

'We didn't make love.' Jared said thickly, his eyes riveted to her face. 'Nessa got changed and showered in her bathroom while I drank a beer and tried to come to terms with the hell this weekend has been.'

'For me, too!' Christie said brokenly.

There was a commotion in the drive as an ambulance siren wailed up it towards the house. Guests murmured excitedly, some moving to the doorway as the ambulance screeched to a halt, doors slammed, and running footsteps came from the marble corridors.

'Don't move!' Jared commanded sharply when Simon tried to sit up.

'Too much pain...' he said threadily, holding his chest. 'Couldn't move if I wanted to. But Ness, my darling Ness—promise you'll come with me to the hospital! I couldn't bear to die away from you!'

'Oh, God, don't say that!' she sobbed, holding him. 'We've been so stupid, both of us. I can't imagine a world without you, even though I've lived without your love for so long! Simon, please forgive me, tell me you love me——'

'I love you desperately, Ness, I always have.'

The paramedics were running into the ballroom with a stretcher and cardiac arrest equipment. 'Clear the way! Get back!'

Jared got to his feet, shouting, 'The patient's over here! His heart's still going, but he's in bad shape——'

'OK, we've got him!' They put the stretcher down, one of them took Jared's place at his side to examine him while the equipment was hooked up to him.

'Oh, Simon, Simon...!' Nessa sobbed in horror as she watched electrodes being fastened to his chest, oxygen mask over his mouth and nose, and then his body lifted on to the stretcher, all in a matter of seconds by the super-efficient team.

He groped for her hand, saying in a muffled voice, 'Don't leave me again, Ness, please! Stay with me at the hospital so I can propose to you when I'm better.'

'What about Christie?' Nessa gripped his hand, crying, 'I love you, darling, but you are engaged to——'

'No,' Christie said huskily. 'Our engagement has been over for most of the weekend. We just didn't want to cause any gossip by announcing it while we were all still here.'

Jared sucked in his breath, staring at her, those dark eyes blazing like black fire.

'Clear the way!' The paramedic team lifted the stretcher and the equipment, beginning to stride fast across the ballroom.

'I'm coming with him, is that OK?' Nessa ran after them, and began giving details to a female paramedic as she clung to Simon's hand, and the whole procession disappeared around the corner and out of the ballroom.

CHAPTER TEN

CHRISTIE stood opposite Jared, her heart beating with sudden fierce, wild hope. Simon was safe now, and his love had been restored to him. But so had hers. She believed it so overwhelmingly as she stared into Jared's strong handsome face and saw her love returned in those passionate eyes of his. Her mind was working at top speed, now that the danger was over, and it was replaying everything Jared had said. 'I believed what you said to me this afternoon . . . I really asked for a slug in the guts . . . saw your passionate embrace . . .'

Jared was staring at her, too. His eyes were intent on hers, but she could see the thoughts flickering behind them like information on a dark computer screen, and she knew he was remembering everything she'd said to him, all weekend, his doubts beginning to slide away in the face of the enormous revelation of her fake engagement to Simon since they got here.

Hope ran wild in her heart, in her eyes, love written all over her face as she kept thinking, He said he had begun to believe me, to respect and admire and love, he must love me, he must, must love me . . .

'Is it true?' Jared asked thickly. 'Has your engagement really been over for most of the weekend?'

'I tried to tell you this afternoon, but I couldn't say it out loud, not even to convince you.' Her voice was shaking. She didn't dare say too much, even now, in case he rejected her again, but she couldn't believe he would, not with that look in his eyes as the hard, hating

Jared began to fade and the passionate, loving Jared was resurrected in his dark eyes.

'And the kiss?' he asked roughly. 'I saw you from the balcony——'

'Because I saw you,' she whispered. 'And I couldn't bear it, so I just turned to Simon for comfort. I was crying, Jared, not kissing.'

He breathed unsteadily. 'You should have told me the engagement was over. Why didn't you tell me that?'

'I gave my word to Simon that I wouldn't tell anyone!'

'I made a similar promise to Nessa.'

Christie's heart beat faster with hope. 'You—you mean what you said this afternoon was true? That you're friends and nothing more?'

'Nessa and I only have one thing in common apart from the film industry. We both had our hearts broken by the people we loved.'

'Loved?' Her heart was banging violently. 'You—you mean you don't love those people any more?'

'If Nessa can admit she still loves the man who broke her heart, I guess I can admit...' He drew a harsh breath. 'I guess...' He closed his eyes.

She reached out a shaking hand. 'Jared...' Without thinking, she heard herself say, 'I love you.'

His eyes flashed open. His hand grasped hers tight. He pulled her into his arms.

'Jared!' Tears stung her eyes as she was enfolded in his powerful embrace. 'Oh, God, my darling...'

'I love you!' he muttered hoarsely into her neck. 'I've never stopped loving you—even when I was hating you!'

She clung to him, unable to believe she could feel such joy. 'I wanted to say "I love you" this afternoon. It was what I came to say, but I was so afraid; you were so curt, disbelieving, cynical——'

'Please forgive me for doubting you. I knew you were telling the truth, knew your love was real, but I couldn't

bear to be a fool again, couldn't bear to believe you only
to find that you were manipulating and——'

'Don't apologise . . . love means never having to say
you're sorry!'

He groaned, and a second later their mouths were
seeking each other, the kiss so necessary as the darkness
was finally smashed aside by the sunlight of love, and
they kissed deeply, drowningly, holding each other tight
enough to merge together.

Millie laughed softly behind them, drawling, 'Ah . . .
another successful weekend at Casa Camarra!'

They broke apart to find everyone staring at them with
indulgent smiles. Christie went scarlet with embarrassment, burying her face in Jared's strong neck.

We like to think,' said Mike, 'that mixing business
with pleasure can often be a very profitable experience.'

Millie nudged his fat stomach. 'Not profitable, darling.
They'll think you want them to make a film together!'

Jared laughed, so did Christie, and as they looked at
Mike and Millie they saw that they had been the real
manipulators all along.

'Come on,' Jared said to Christie under his breath,
'let's go somewhere more private and talk. Hollywood
already has enough information on us after this to last
a lifetime.' He turned her in his arms, and together they
walked briskly, almost running, out of the ballroom.

Everyone watched them go, an excited babble of conversation starting up even before they had disappeared.

'Music!' Millie cried to the band.

'What about Simon?' Mike asked. 'Or should we just
ring the hospital in a few . . .'

The conversation drifted away into music as the band
started up again, and Jared and Christie turned the
corner into the vast, glittering marble hallway again.

'My bedroom?' Jared said softly, holding her hand,
long fingers linking with hers.

She flushed, excited, breathless. 'Yes...'

They went up the stairs. 'We can ring the hospital in an hour or so, see how Simon's doing. I should think they'll just give him a lot of tests first.'

She nodded. 'Do you think he's going to pull through?' Concern tinged her voice. 'He looked so ill...'

'I think he'll be fine. It looked like a twinge to me, a murmur. The heart was still beating erratically, but it wasn't dangerously fast, and it certainly hadn't stopped. I expect they'll give him some drugs, and some tests, but I'll be very surprised if he isn't out and about within a week.'

'Speaking of tests,' she said huskily as they passed Vivien Leigh, 'is it safe to assume that your demands for the casting couch are off now?'

His eyes darted to hers. 'Darling, I'm sorry if that hurt you. I can see now that it must have done quite dreadfully.'

'I've been through hell,' she confessed, eyes pained suddenly.

He stopped on the stairs, his hand holding hers. 'So have I. I can't quite believe the barriers are finally down, but we mustn't stop and think about it, or they might slide up again.'

She nodded, aware that he was right. 'Yes... we have to just take this as it comes, don't we?'

'And trust each other,' he said deeply, 'as you trusted me this afternoon by the pool.'

Christie flushed, and lowered her lashes.

'I know I was a heel to you,' he said thickly, 'while you cried and made yourself vulnerable to me. I was completely convinced, but at the same time so afraid to let you see I believed you. When all was said and done, you *were* still officially engaged to Simon, and no amount of talk about "old friends" could change that.'

'Yes, I can understand that.' She smiled suddenly and squeezed his hand. 'Come on. Let's just carry on like this, complete trust and belief in each other. No more suspicion or hatred.'

He kissed her, smiled, and then they carried on up the stairs, along the corridor.

Christie walked beside him, not quite believing fully her good fortune in the way events had changed her whole view of life again. Thank God Simon hadn't had a serious heart attack. If he was sensible, he might never have another one, and he now had Nessa by his side, in love with him, prepared to stay with him forever.

A smile touched her mouth. 'It was nice to see Nessa and Simon getting back together again, wasn't it?'

'She was crazy about him,' Jared agreed, his arm slung casually around her shoulders as they walked along the corridor to his bedroom door. 'I don't think she ever mentioned another man's name to me, in all the three years we've been friends.'

Jealousy flared in her again, and she shot a savage look at him. 'How did you meet her?'

Jared smiled and stopped walking, bending his head to kiss her mouth. 'Don't be jealous, darling. Nessa was always just someone for me to go to when my own savage jealousy got too much.'

'Savage jealousy...?'

He laughed. 'Really savage! Don't forget, for the last three years I've had to sit back and watch you soar up the Hollywood superladder with Simon Mordant at your side.'

'Oh, yes...!' She stared into his wild, dark eyes. 'If you still loved me all that time, then it must have been hell.'

'It was a complete nightmare, darling!' he confessed, arching black brows and holding her close as they stood in front of the bedroom door, bodies very close, faces almost touching. 'And Nessa was my strongest support. We used to scream at the television together sometimes, when you and Simon came on chat shows, holding hands, every inch the beautiful Hollywood couple.'

She gasped in amazed wonder. 'Did you...!'

'I fear so!' he drawled, laughing. 'Very childish, but there you are. When you're in love, these things come blasting out from the darkness, and civilised men turn into savage infants.'

'Darling...!' She stroked his neck, love filling her eyes. 'I can barely believe it. All these years.' Pain struck at her as she leant against his powerful body. 'And did you feel it all again when you first saw me here at Casa Camarra?'

'Yes...' He gave a harsh sigh, and kissed her head. 'Yes, I felt it all. But I also felt anger, fear and hatred. A nasty mess and very difficult to deal with. Especially when you're in love.'

Her eyes closed as she whispered, 'I've been so lonely, Jared. So very lost without you...'

'Well, you're not lost any more,' he said huskily, and bent his head to kiss her, his mouth burning over hers, parting her lips with infinite tenderness and making her heart quicken as she returned his kiss, eyes closing, blonde head tilting back.

He drew her closer in his arms. The kiss grew more passionate. Soon, they were giving hoarse, fierce exclamations of growing desire, and then Jared dragged his mouth from hers with a groan.

'We'd better go inside,' he said thickly, releasing her and opening the door. 'Before this gets out of hand.'

She stepped inside, into the dark, masculine bedroom with its polished-wood floor, long dark red couch, and discreet dim gold lighting in the form of art deco lamps on dark wood furniture.

Her eyes flicked to the four-poster bed.

Jared closed the door, leaning on it, watching her through heavy eyelids. 'The casting couch...' he murmured softly.

She turned to look at him, her heart banging nineteen to the dozen. 'Oh, Jared, it's been so long!'

Dark colour invaded his face as he stepped towards her, and as the light glowed behind them, he took her in his arms, his hot mouth bearing down on hers, compelling a breathless moan and fierce response as her hands linked around his strong neck.

Desire flared between them like lightning on a summer day. Her body was pressing fiercely against his, revelling in the feel of the strong muscles, the rigid hardness of his manhood against her flat belly, and the way his hands slid swiftly down to cup her rear as they kissed with blind, delirious passion.

'Oh, God, Chris...my darling!' he said hoarsely against her bruised mouth. 'We've wasted so much time! I can't believe how I hated you the way I did! When all along it was just so simple! You weren't Simon's lover, you didn't leave me for him, you loved me and——'

'Was it really that simple?' she asked huskily, stroking his dark handsome cheek. 'Don't forget that you wanted me to be the perfect wife and mother—while I wanted to be what I am now.'

'An internationally successful film star. An Academy Award-winning actress. You can't imagine how galling it was for me to stand back and watch you do it all, single-handed, without so much as an inch of help from me. I felt utterly emasculated sometimes, as though you were doing it deliberately, just to teach me what an arrogant chauvinistic fool I was.'

Christie's lashes flicked in disbelief. 'You mean—you admit it?'

His hard mouth crooked in a self-deprecating smile. 'Chris, I can't hope to make this work if I don't. And we have to discuss that whole mess I made about the perfect woman, or you and I will come unstuck again at the first bridge we try to cross.'

She nodded slowly, scarcely able to believe her ears. After all this time, he was ready to put down the illusions of childhood, illusions he had every justification to cling to, given the sad circumstances of his upbringing. But he was right—if he didn't let go of them, they would never make it. If they were to get together again, it would have to be on a very different basis.

'The last three years have taught me what a fool I was,' Jared said deeply. 'I had other women, as I told you—several at first, because I was so unhappy.'

Jealousy darkened her eyes. 'You slept with all of them?'

'No. Just one or two.'

She lowered her lashes, trying to conceal the way she felt, knowing it was unreasonable to be jealous, yet unable to help it.

'I picked sweet, wholesome, ordinary women,' Jared said deeply, his arms around her slender, beautiful body in the pale satin gown that shrieked glamorous film star. 'I had long relationships with them, all of them. Got them to cook for me, wash my clothes, look after me the way I thought a real woman should.' He sighed, shaking his dark head. 'And I was fond of all of them, terribly fond. But I didn't love them. And, worse than that, I couldn't even hold a conversation with any of them.'

She risked a quick look up into his eyes, holding her breath, praying he was going to say what she thought he was going to say: that he understood now that he would never be happy with anyone who couldn't share his excitement of life, his need for adventure and achievement, and his rage against the injustices of the past. That rage had long since died, she knew that. He would hardly be adult if he still harboured it deep inside him. But its energy had carried him to the top, and made him what he was today. How could any ordinary woman from an ordinary, happy family ever hope to understand the demons that had coloured his entire life from infancy to adulthood, creating Jared Buchanan, universally respected film director, out of the hurt, angry little boy who had grown up in that orphanage?

'I tried so hard to make my relationships with them work,' Jared said deeply. 'Both here and in England. I told myself every night that they were what I wanted, what I'd spent my life dreaming of, and that we would have wonderful, happy children who would have the mother I never had, and the home I always needed.'

Christie listened, her eyes filled with love and understanding.

'But, of course,' he said thickly, 'in the darkest hours of the night, when I needed someone close to me who understood without being told, who knew what I had been through without having to be given a step-by-step guide book to the whole emotional journey...' His eyes darkened with passionate love. 'That was when I missed you the most, Chris.'

'Darling...' She kissed his handsome mouth.

'You always knew, didn't you?' he said huskily. 'Right from the minute our eyes met in that newsagent's. Do you remember?'

'Across the greetings cards stand!' she laughed softly. 'Of course I remember, darling! You were staring at me intently, as though I were a prize you wanted to fight for, and I remember feeling excited at the thought of such a powerfully driven man. It was there in your eyes. The way they narrowed with determination as you watched me. I could see you were a fighter, a winner——'

'Like that song,' he said softly. 'My favourite song—remember? About the boxer who remembers every punch, every cut, every moment of anger—and fuels himself with them to get to the top.'

She stroked his hard cheek. 'You're such a very strong man, darling. Your one weakness was always the vision of perfection in a woman. And I used to feel so frightened when we lived together. I knew one day it would rise up and come between us, drive us apart, because however much I loved you, I knew I could never *be* that woman. I could only be exactly who I am.'

'And I've learned to love you for that,' he said deeply. 'It was a lesson I badly needed to be taught, too. I saw that, in the end. When I'd finally come to the end of my tether with the very lovely women I tried to fall in love with. I just sat back and gave up, and said to myself, you bloody idiot. That kind of woman will never understand what makes you tick, and you'll never have a hope of understanding her, either. There's only one woman who can hope to understand a crazy, complicated, ambitious misfit like you, and you threw her away out of pride and stupidity!'

Christie smiled into his eyes. 'But I'm back, darling? See? And I'm never going to leave you again.'

'But you did leave me,' he said thickly. 'Didn't you, Chris? It wasn't just because you knew you couldn't live up to my idea of the perfect woman, now was it?'

She flushed, the smile fading from her face. 'No...and you've been completely honest with me, darling. So the least I can do is be as honest with you.'

His dark lashes flickered. A smile grew on his handsome mouth as he held her in loving silence, waiting, although he must have known what was going to come, because he understood her even better than she could ever have suspected. He understood because he was like her, in so many ways, and he loved her for all of them.

'I . . .' Her voice was husky suddenly as she faced the prospect of her own love confession. 'Well, I was so ambitious, Jared. When you gave me that ultimatum, it was the last straw in a series of straws that broke my back.'

He nodded slowly. 'You resented me for expecting perfection from you, all along.'

'Yes.' She looked down at the powerful width of his chest beneath the white shirt and black evening jacket. 'It just built up. I don't know how or when or why— just that I kept silent so many times. You used to wax lyrical about how women should be. The clothes they should wear in public, the way they should treat their men, always loving and deferential, as though their men were somehow superior to them.'

'I was a fool,' he said thickly, pain in his eyes. 'And I'm sorry I ever thought like that.'

She sighed softly. 'It wasn't your fault.'

'Yes, it was, Chris. And you must never cosset me again by either thinking that or saying it to me. If I've learned anything in the last three years without you, it's that I must be responsible for my own thoughts and feelings, and not continually lean on my deprivation as a child in order to explain them away to myself or the woman I love.' He smiled and drawled, 'The woman who puts up with me, I should say. You were quite justified in objecting to my behaviour, darling. So don't tell me it wasn't my fault.'

'All right,' she said, playing with his tie, her smile very wide as she felt less and less worried about the confession she had to make. 'And you're right—I resented you bitterly. Apart from anything else, I'd been brought up on a similar diet of female perfection. Whenever you criticised my behaviour as a woman in the home, I felt attacked, and I also felt guilty. I did believe, partly, that you were right. That's why I tried to bite my tongue whenever I felt angry and wanted to throw something at you, scream that you were a selfish, arrogant male chauvinist pig who deserved——'

'Yes, I get the picture!' he drawled, laughing softly and nuzzling her throat with his mouth. 'And next time I do it—if I'm ever stupid enough to do it again, which I doubt—please feel free to hurl the nearest saucepan at me and tell me to do the cooking myself.' He lifted his head, eyes wry. 'As I did when you walked out on me.'

She bit her lip, eyes loving. 'Oh, did you, darling? Did you really? I can't imagine you cooking in the kitchen! You were so utterly opposed to it.'

'I had to learn that men and women aren't defined by stereotypes.'

Her lashes flickered and she said slowly, 'My God, yes... that's exactly what I had to learn.'

He waited, arms holding her, eyes loving and patient.

'You see, darling,' she began unsteadily, 'when I walked out on the man I loved——'

He kissed her nose tenderly.

'I felt compelled to behave in a faintly unfeminine way.' Her eyes flickered up, seeking and finding understanding. 'It was as though I completely rejected the woman in me. I was a career girl now, I said to myself, and the only thing I lived for was ambition. Mountains to climb, awards to win, people to impress—that kind of thing. There was no room in my life, or my heart, for love. I certainly never even thought about love-making. The very idea would have been ludicrous. My body was for the screen, for the gym, to be honed to perfection with four-hour daily workouts, endless dieting, and perfectly fitted glamorous clothes. It was to be admired, looked at, worshipped—but not touched.'

'It...' he said softly, arching black brows.

She stared at him for a long moment in astonishment. 'Oh,' she said huskily, shocked, 'yes, I see what you mean.'

'You completely lost touch with yourself as a human female,' he murmured deeply, and there was pain in his eyes which told her he understood. 'Forgot that you were not made for career alone, but for love, lovemaking, child-bearing——'

'Oh, darling!' she whispered unsteadily, clutching his broad shoulders. 'I really did reject myself as a woman when I left you, didn't I? How obvious it seems to me now! More obvious than it ever has over the last three years of work, work, work. All that ambition, and look what it did to me! I lived a completely one-sided life, without a thought for my feelings or the needs of my body! I just drove myself endlessly in the pursuit of——'

'Fame,' he said gently. 'The same thing as me. And don't ever hate yourself for it, darling, or feel angry about it. Don't forget it's one of the reasons we are able to love and understand each other. That's worth more than any regret. The only problem you encountered was that you weren't experienced enough in life to make sure everything balanced.'

She frowned, studying him thoughtfully, knowing there was something important in what he said.

'I learned a long time ago,' he told her softly, 'that you have to balance your life. You need work, sure, especially if you're very ambitious. And you need achievements. Milestones, if you like, in a long road leading to whatever your final goal happens to be. That way, you know you're getting there. You get the thrill of success, without the final reward, and it keeps you going.' He laughed. 'Like a chocolate bar when you need instant energy!'

Christie laughed too, relaxing in his arms, blue eyes shining. 'Oh, those chocolate bars! Darling, you can't imagine how thrilled I was with Oscar! I just felt like the cat's miaow!'

'You are the cat's miaow!' he drawled softly, kissing her full pink lips. 'And I want to see you win best actress with *Tigresse*.'

Her eyes widened. She hesitated, tensing in his arms, because the very mention of that film was now enough to send her into paranoid panic, every memory connected to it bringing back feelings of fear, distrust and loneliness.

'Hey,' he said softly, reading her expression, 'you know that I love you, don't you? And that my love goes right down to the bone.'

She paused, then nodded, still afraid of the mention of that wretched film.

'And you know,' he said, kissing her, 'that I'm very proud of you. Of your work, I mean. The quality of your acting, and the way you've carved this very big niche for yourself, out here in my world, the film industry: Hollywood.'

Flushing with pride, she nodded, a smile beginning to appear on her full lips as she felt the trust coming back, bringing love with it like a sunlit tidal wave.

'And you also know,' he smiled lazily, 'that you're the perfect choice for the role of Lelie. Now—no bad memories, darling, and no false modesty. Come on, now. Be the woman I love, and am proud of, and want to see succeed on her own terms, her own merit, her own talent . . .'

Christie lifted her head, a cool smile on her full mouth and a very amused, ambitious, loving, self-assured look in her tiger-lily eyes.

'Yes . . .' he said thickly, still smiling, but with a trace of sexual excitement at this display of her personality at its most powerful. 'Oh, yes, Christie McCall. You *will* play Lelie the Tigresse in my film, or I can promise you there'll be hell to pay!'

She gave a slow laugh of incredulous pleasure, which turned to deep emotion, tears stinging her eyes as she buried her face in his strong neck with waves of love flooding through her heart.

'Oh, Jared!' she whispered huskily. 'I can't believe you're treating me as an equal! I respected you so much, still do, always will, and I was so afraid you despised me, looked down on me...'

'But you know I don't, you must know,' he said thickly against her hair. 'And you know I never really did.' He lifted his dark head, looking her in the eye. 'You do know that, don't you?'

'I know it now,' she confessed huskily, and he shook his head.

'No, you knew it then, Chris. Or I would not have been the man to take your virginity.'

She studied him in breathless wonder, suddenly seeing his thought process and understanding it.

'You were twenty-five years old when I met you,' Jared said softly. 'Beautiful, sexy, charming, intelligent and loving...yet no man had ever got further than a kiss with you. Why? No, don't tell me, darling. I already know—or at least, I think I do. I've had a chance to think deep and hard about it over the last three years, and the answer I've finally come up with is that you may look like a sex bomb, but the truth is, you're a love bomb.'

She laughed softly, lowering her lashes.

'A lot of women are interested in nothing but men,' he said deeply. 'They spend their lives thinking about boyfriends, taking boyfriends, sleeping with boyfriends, talking about boyfriends—nothing but men, men, men, their whole lives through.' His dark eyes studied her with deep love and understanding. 'But you, Chris... you're only interested in two things. Your dreams—and your integrity.'

'Darling, I fell in love with you when I first saw you,' she whispered. 'I was in that newsagent's, dreaming—just as I always did. Dream, dream, dream... of all my successes, my glories, the films I'd make and the awards I'd win. Then I looked up with an I've-just-won-ten-Oscars smile, and saw you staring at me. I felt my heart miss a beat, and thought, Good heavens! A man!'

He laughed like mad, his voice husky.

'Then you followed me out of the shop, and I thought, Oooh! This is the first time I've ever wanted a man to try and chat me up!'

He laughed again, kissing her neck.

Christie lifted her face, smiling. 'You did chat me up. You chatted me up very thoroughly. And I thought, Hello! He really is gorgeous! I wonder who he is and what he does—and then, I wonder what it's like to be kissed by him...'

His smile faded slowly, heart beginning to thud like a drum as he stared down into her face and sexual desire suddenly sprang at them with a fierce hiss of steam and heat and intolerable necessity.

'Oh, God, Chris...' he said thickly as she felt that powerful manhood spring into hard excitement against her belly.

She was breathing thickly, her heart banging violently as she ran her hands over his powerful chest, her mind filling suddenly with vivid, searing images of their nudity.

'I forgot what it was to be a woman,' she said huskily. 'I forgot until I saw you again, here, at Casa Camarra. I've been so lost, Jared. So hopelessly lost in the fog of ambition, and I drove myself too hard, too fast, never letting myself stop for a minute in case I found I was a failure as a woman——'

'You were never a failure as a woman,' he said thickly. 'You were just young and needed time to come to terms with who you really were, what you really wanted out of life. Just as I needed that time, too. We met too soon, Chris, that's all it comes down to. We just met too soon for either of us to cope with love, let alone a marriage of equals.'

'Yes, I can see that that's true.' She was trembling against him, her body powerfully aware of his, and of the sexual need vibrating between them as they struggled to talk, struggled not to take any notice of the throbbing of the blood, the desire in the mind, and the fire in the loins, the necessity, the hot, driving necessity to couple and mate. 'And maybe that's a part of my own mistakes—the mistakes I made with you. I was so determined to be successful that I sometimes felt I had to be a man to do it. To be like a man. To drive and drive, push and push, be determined and fierce and utterly uncompromising.'

'But nature didn't build your body like a man's,' he said thickly, hands sliding over her rear, fondling her, making the desire and necessity burn her until she felt her clothes almost sizzle. 'So after your passionate and uninhibited affair with me you couldn't cope unless you just shut the whole desire channel down.'

'No, I couldn't,' she said, her hands firm and hungry and filled with desire as they moved over his shoulders, her eyes glazed as she stared at his body. 'And I could only channel my drive into my career, and pretend to be capable of marrying without love, or desire, or physical needs. Simon and I loved each other as friends, allies—but not man and woman.'

'And how do you love me?' he asked fiercely.

'As a woman,' she said in an ardent, shaking voice as her arms linked around his neck and guided his head down. 'Body, mind, heart and soul!'

His dark head swooped down.

Their mouths met fiercely.

They were both ready...

CHAPTER ELEVEN

THEY clung fiercely, their mouths almost on fire, bodies pressing together, and she didn't want to think any more or talk any more, she just wanted his flesh moving against hers, making her a woman again for the first time in years, making her moan in pleasure at his ultimate male possession, so exquisitely barbaric as the male imposed himself on the female, and her mouth was open beneath his in symbolic acceptance of this ultimate truth of nature, her hands sliding through his thick black hair as she accepted him, accepted herself, accepted sexual destiny and everything it brought with it: love, peace, serenity, children, a home, a family...they were all quite apart from career, she saw that now, and they did not have to impose on ambition. She could be who she was in every area of her life so long as Jared loved her, stayed with her, made love to her...

He lifted her in his arms, carried her to the bed, his mouth inviting wanton behaviour as he licked her lips with his tongue, provoking the uninhibited in her, the animal.

'Oh, Jared,' she whispered thickly as he slid her down on to the bed.

He groaned deep in his throat, sliding his body on top of hers, and began to caress her, to undress her slowly with his fingers and his expertise, teasing a wanton response as he toyed with the straps of her dress, licking her lips, moving his hard male body against hers and giving a cool, sexy sound of excitement when she slowly slid her slender thighs to accommodate him. Now her hands were moving through his hair, and all was natural, animal, provocative—she was joining in the game, playing with him, sliding her hands up and down his back, making him groan harshly as her hands reached his taut buttocks, softly encouraging his body to press hard against hers for a second before her fingers skipped away in feminine dance, back up to his neck, making him shiver and kiss her deeper, tiring of the game, wanting to take control, really take control, show her exactly who was the man and who was the woman...

She moaned long and low as he turned her slightly, tugging down her zip, tugging down the beautiful satin dress.

'Very sexy...' he said thickly as her bare breasts bounced free, and she moaned, knowing he was taking control, wanting him to, needing him to as she let him make her helpless by keeping the straps of the dress momentarily at her wrists while his strong hands cupped those full, aching breasts and stroked the fiercely erect nipples.

'Oh Jared...' she said incoherently, eyes closing, her body arching, free and willing and hot.

His dark head bent. His hot mouth closed over one nipple, sucking hungrily, sending hot needles of piercing sexual excitement through her body as she moved even closer against him, her hands deliberately helpless at her sides, the freedom she felt from the constraints of stereotypes in reality far outweighing the dangers of sexual stereotypes. She felt his hands moving downwards, stroking the thick satin material up her thighs, teasing it up, making her moan in anticipation.

He licked at her bare breast, let his fingers slid between her spread thighs, and then he touched the burning, engorged, intolerably hot nub of flesh between them.

'Ah...ah...!' She was breathless, twisting beneath him, her eyes closed and the tendons standing out in her neck, succumbing to her true womanhood at last, at the hands of a powerful man, a man who loved and understood her, a man who could fight her on every level and a man who could admire her success without being threatened by it.

This man could make her a woman.

She champed at the bit, in this, her final race. She was twisting like molten fire beneath him, yearning to feel those strong, long fingers sliding inside her silky briefs, longing for flesh on flesh, and everything natural.

Slowly, he slid those briefs down, making her moan in wet heat, her heart banging furiously as she waited, waited, felt his fingers stroking her inner thighs, sliding upwards, upwards, upwards...

'Touch me...' she whispered in hoarse urgency.

He did. She almost cried out in pleasure, but his hard mouth silenced her before she could draw agonised breath, and he kissed her deeply as she moaned in ecstasy beneath his expert touch. The long finger stroked that burning nub between her thighs, and she felt her excitement spiralling higher and higher, then the swift slide to move inside her, making her gasp insensibly, her mouth parting as surely as her thighs to receive such pleasure...

When his finger moved back up to stroke her more sensitive flesh, she grew impatient to feel him inside her. Him. All of him—that long-forgotten but fiercely remembered hard jut of flesh that made him man—and she wanted it so badly she was shaking, her fingers barely able to move the tie from that strong throat, or the buttons from that white shirt.

He shrugged out of his jacket, never lifting his mouth from hers, and she pushed his shirt off, moaning against his mouth in rising excitement. Oh, God, here was his

flesh, that tanned, taut flesh across hard muscle, black
hairs matting his chest as she stripped him to the waist,
then began to lower her hands, slowly, exploringly, all
over his powerful torso as he kissed her deeply, stroked
her expertly, and prepared her with his love and sexual
skill for the moment they needed to share so badly.

'Darling...' She could barely speak, her voice clogged
with deep, animal breaths of desire. 'Oh, make love to
me...take me...oh, yes, take me, Jared...Jared!'

He moved against her, kissing her, stroking her, licking
her lips, one hand between her wet, shaking thighs, the
other sliding under her rear to cup her bare buttocks and
press her gently, slowly against the fierce hardness between his own thighs.

She almost went mad, kissing him passionately, ready
to beg, but enjoying this, strangely, because the excitement was so strong, so deep, and so fulfilling after
all this time, making her feel the dust falling from her
body as it came to life under his body, his hands, until
she was pulsing with life, radiant with it, pulsating from
head to foot with rich, natural sensuality.

Suddenly, as though he knew she was ready, his right
hand went to his trouser button, flicking it open as he
continued to kiss and stroke her, then the flare of the
zip, and she was moaning low and hoarse with anticipation as he slowly, skilfully, pushed his clothes down
to let that powerful, throbbing manhood free to burn
against her inner thigh.

'Oh, God...!' she whispered thickly, and her hands
sought him without thinking. He filled her hand, a thick,
hot symbol of the male power, and she thrilled to feel
it in her fingers, pulsing with hot blood, rigid as steel.

He was nude now, and so was she, their clothes now
discarded, completely irrelevant, nothing mattering but
the fact that they were in love, and love made this
natural, good, right...

'Tell me you want me, baby!' he said thickly, sliding naked against her, tormenting her with his hard, hair-roughened flesh. 'Tell me you love me...'

'Oh, yes, I love you!' she breathed hotly, kissing him, sliding her tongue over his neck. 'I really want you...and I want to prove it, let you feel it without words...' She slid her kiss over his neck, down to his chest, and he began to breathe faster as he realised what she was going to do, began to stiffen, his body thrusting forwards and vibrating in hot, disbelief, a long low moan coming from his throat as her mouth slid down, down, down...

'Chris!' He gasped out as she took him in her hot, sensual mouth. 'Oh, baby...!' He clutched her head, his body thrown forwards in fierce excitement as she rolled him with her wet tongue, inciting hoarse moans of terrible pleasure. 'Darling...yes, yes, yes...!'

As she lifted her head, eyes dazed with love and freedom, she licked her lips unconsciously, and Jared gave a low growl, his face running with fierce red colour.

'Your turn to say yes!' he bit out thickly, and slid her on to her back again, moving on top of her, flicking her thighs apart with deliberate mimicry of absolute male domination and, as she felt his power, she moaned out loud, arching her body in acceptance and submission, feeling the sudden hot thrust of him at her wet, wet entrance.

He slid inside with one slow thrust. Christie cried out, shaking. So did he. They breathed harshly, staring dazedly into each other's eyes. Then his finger began to seek and stroke that hot nub of excited flesh between her thighs, his voice began to whisper wicked things, and soon she was gasping higher, faster...

'Yes, yes, yes!' She jerked against him with a guttural cry of pleasure.' Her body threw itself all over him, spasming and flooding with heat, wetness, gasping out his name thickly on one broad powerful shoulder as he held her tight, still stroking her, struggling to keep control himself as she vaguely, through her pleasure, sensed his body tensing like a ramrod and beginning to shake with the extent of his excitement and the growing necessity of release.

She shuddered to a limp, breathless stop beneath him. Her thighs were trembling like crazy. She couldn't breathe, couldn't move her neck, just stared into space as her eyes refocused and she realised her nails were biting deeply into his shoulders.

Jared dragged air into his lungs, his heart banging violently as he suddenly realised she was released, and started to move against her, slowly at first while his hands clutched her rear, then growing faster, faster, until he was pummelling her repeatedly with harsh growls of desire burning in his throat . . . and then he gave a shout of pure agony and jerked against her, unmoving for split-seconds, then drawing back with another sucking in of agonised breath, before thrusting back into her, fingers biting into her hips as his excitement burst into her, spurting into her womb with life-giving force, and then a third time, until he collapsed, gasping for breath, on her shoulder.

They lay like that, two stranded fish without air, struggling for it for minutes as their heartbeats thundered between them and through the room, their bodies warm and damp with sweat.

'I love you,' Jared gasped out unexpectedly without lifting his head, then laughed huskily. 'I can't look at you, darling . . . I feel as though I'll die if I try to move!'

She laughed breathlessly and stroked his hair, astonished to find it wet, almost saturated with the sweat of his excitement as he had made love to her with such fire and consideration.

'Me, too,' she whispered huskily. 'I'm so tired I can't even breathe. But I love you . . . very much.'

'Think you can forgive me everything?' he asked deeply. 'Even the way I spoke to you about the casting couch?'

She laughed softly, playing with his hair. 'Of course I can! You were only being defensive, not trying to hurt me. And I could see so clearly why you thought as you did, darling.'

'Could you, darling?' He raised his head then, concern in his dark eyes. 'I was so vicious to you. Said such terrible things. And I know when I said them I meant every word of them. Don't tell me they didn't hurt you, because——'

'They devastated me,' she said truthfully, looking into his eyes. 'But you had so many good reasons to believe I was that kind of a woman. Those love-games I played with you three years ago were so exciting—but, in retrospect, they did look damning. And I couldn't help thinking—that's all he wanted from me.'

'It was the same for me,' he admitted with a grimace. 'The trouble was that I was so influenced by the script of this damned film. Darling, you know how it is when you get involved in a project. It takes you over, colours your whole life until it's finished. And the character of Lelie was so close to what I'd told myself you were. Even though I'd learned my lesson and was already coming to terms with my own faults, my own responsibilities for what went wrong between us. I still looked at you and saw Lelie…' He sighed deeply. 'Maybe it was just casting, but then again——'

'Maybe it was what you were most afraid of,' she said softly. 'I understand, darling. And, looking back, it's easy to see why that was such a strong possibility. I didn't leave you because of my career, but it was one major reason why our relationship faltered.'

He smiled, kissing her. 'It's amazing, isn't it, to think we were only together for six months. Yet those six months changed and influenced both our lives for three years—and, hopefully, will continue to influence them for many to come...'

Christie looked deep into his eyes, her heart thudding with hope, with fear, with love. She knew what she wanted, needed to hear, but was afraid...this was the last vestige of womanhood, this: the proposal of marriage from a man she loved. She was a career girl from way back, ambition burned into her soul through hardship and lack of love, mockery in the playground and in the home. It was hard for her to accept that she needed marriage, domesticity, a husband, love and a home. So easy to accept the great, glittering career which shrouded her in a golden haze and dispelled the inferiorities of her childhood, made her feel special, loved, different, unique. Marriage was something quite different. It was the affirmation of normality, of being like everyone else, of being real and human and ordinary. Everyone got married. Stars lived sad, disturbed, unbalanced lives. But Christie didn't want her life to be like that. She wanted to Have It All, because if she didn't get it all, she knew that was how she would end up—like all the stars that had gone before her, or at least the majority of them: women without love, without hope, without normality. Maybe that was the key to it. Normality. She needed to feel normal, and ordinary. A woman, not a star. A wife, not a sex symbol. A mother, not an icon.

Jared looked deep into her eyes, for he must have known more than anyone what a test this was, and exactly what he was about to demand of her, for all his love and understanding.

'Darling,' he said deeply, unsteadily, 'will you marry me?'

She didn't even hesitate. 'Yes!' she whispered huskily, bowing her head to his realness, his humanity. 'Yes, Jared...I will marry you, my darling.'

He groaned and kissed her deeply, tenderly, for he understood, they both understood that this was a moment unprecedented in either of their lives, a moment of acceptance of their own humanity, and that however famous, rich, powerful they ever became, there was only one reality for either of them—that they would one day die, be taken back to the earth, be buried ashes to ashes, dust to dust...and only the children of their union would survive.

They must have children. That was the true immortality. In the end, there was no other. All the oil paintings in Casa Camarra, all the Oscars, all the money, all the power in the world could not change that simple fact.

Yes, still they both dreamed...

'Our children,' Jared said wonderingly, kissing her, 'will be stars, millionaires, presidents...'

'And we'll be so proud!' she continued, eyes stinging with tears. 'We'll think of such names for them, such wonderful names, and give them such a send off...'

'But can't you just see it, darling?' he laughed. 'They'll probably hate fame, money, power. They'll turn their backs on it and say, To hell with such artifice! Give me what is real and natural and good! Give me——'

'Love!' she said softly, touching his neck. 'Well, I must admit, I'd be a tad disappointed, but I can't help agreeing with them, even if they're not born yet. If nothing else, our experience together has taught us that only love is important.'

'I agree,' he said deeply.

'I'm glad you do,' she whispered. 'Because we're going to go through hell married to each other. You know that, don't you? You'll be away filming pictures, I'll be at home having babies, and when you get back filled with trophies and dreams and triumphs, I'll probably throw a saucepan at you and start screaming, "What about *my* dreams, *my* trophies and *my* triumphs...!"'

'Well, then,' he said deeply, 'you'd better make your choice before we start. I'm not taking the blame for your life choices. You wouldn't want me to, either. I'll take responsibility for mine, and that's all. But if you decide to give up work and have children ... well, then, that's your choice...'

She made a face. 'Oh ... all right, then!'

He laughed, then sobered, eyes concerned. 'Just be sure, darling. I'd hate to have an unfulfilled wife. And remember—you'll make *Tigresse* before you get pregnant.'

'I might be pregnant now,' she reminded him huskily.

He stared down at her, going pale. 'Oh, God, yes...so you might!'

'What price *Tigresse* then?'

'No...' His hands tightened on her. 'No, I don't believe you're pregnant, yet. It's your destiny to make that film, darling. You were born to play the role of Tigresse. It's your part. You'll shine in it, be superb, win every award on the board ... and when it's done, when all the hullaballoo is over—then you'll get pregnant, my darling, but not before then!'

She laughed, eyes dancing. 'I'm glad you have such——'

The telephone rang.

They stared at it, then at each other.

Jared leaned over, snatched it up. 'Yes ... ah, that's very good news.' His dark eyes flicked to her and she knew suddenly that it was a call about Simon, that he was all right, that he wasn't going to die, and that he was going to be happy. 'Really?' Jared laughed. 'How extraordinary! No, no, of course I won't tell anyone else!'

'What?' Christie demanded silently, her eyes trying to compell him to tell her.

'And everything's going well, is it?' he went on, shushing her with one strong hand. 'Oh, I'm delighted to hear that. Yes...' He looked at Christie with a wicked, loving smile. 'Oh, yes, everything's going wonderfully well here! Mmmm. Well, I don't know about that! But yes, I'm really pleased to hear your news, and I'll certainly pass it on!' He laughed softly, then nodded. 'OK. See you some time tomorrow, then! Bye...!'

Christie watched him replace the phone. 'Well? Who was it? Tell me!'

He laughed, eyes dancing as he drawled, 'That was Nessa, calling from the hospital. She's with Simon, and he's completely in the clear.' He laughed again, saying, 'Guess what? You'll never guess, I know you won't...!'

'What!' she demanded furiously. '*What*!'

'It wasn't a heart attack at all!' he said, laughing again. 'It was indigestion!'

Her mouth gaped open. 'No...!'

'Oh, I'm afraid so!' he drawled, eyes dancing with wicked light. 'All that food Mike made him eat, I'm afraid. It produced the symptoms of a heart attack, and that's why he felt so much pain. But he didn't have a heart attack at all, poor bloke, he just had serious indigestion brought on by too many garlic sausages!' He collapsed with laughter and she went with him, laughing too, because it was such a relief to know Simon was in no real danger at all, even though his predicament was obviously very embarrassing.

'Stop laughing!' she chided Jared. 'It's very naughty of you!'

'I'm sorry,' he returned, still laughing. 'But you must see the funny side of it, Chris!'

'Of course I do,' she reprimanded him. 'But you should see the serious side of it, too. Simon thought he was dying—that's a very serious moment for a man to go through, particularly in such a public situation!'

'Hey...' he said softly. 'I was the one ready to start his heart if it stopped—remember?'

Her eyes filled with pride. 'Yes... and I was so proud of you, Jared. You had every reason to hate Simon then. But you still stepped in ready to save his life...'

'Hmm.' He studied her with a smile, his eyes filled with love. 'Want to hear how they're getting on at the hospital? Nessa and Simon, I mean?'

She nodded at once, eyes intense.

He smiled. 'They're getting married. Right now!'

'What...?'

'Yes—someone is coming to marry them at his bedside, even though he isn't dying, because they feel they've spent too much time apart, and they need to marry right away.'

Christie stared at him as she imagined the scene—Ness and Simon marrying in haste at his bed, and they would not repent in leisure, because they, too, had learned their lesson in love. Maybe everyone had to learn a hard lesson in love, she thought with sudden amazement. Maybe there were more lessons to learn about love than about any other subject known to man or woman, and Nessa and Simon were no exception, with their history of anger and distrust.

'So, all's well,' said Jared in Shakespearean mood, 'that ends well.'

She smiled, relaxing beneath him, her arms around his neck. 'So it does...'

'Darling,' he said softly, 'we have so much to look forward to, if we can only trust each other and remember what we've learnt this time round about love.'

'Yes...' Her eyes darkened.

'Do you think you can do it?' he whispered against her mouth as he began to kiss her lips burningly, possessively. 'We went through hell and there was nobody there to help us, not even our friends, because love is a lesson you can only learn alone, and this time through there's going to be nobody but you and me...!'

'I can handle it,' she said softly, nuzzling his neck with her warm, loving lips, completely a woman now, not interested in career or ambition as long as she was there with him, his woman, the woman he had chosen for his life and his mate and his equal.

'Oh?' His eyes shone with passion. 'What else can you handle?'

'Anything you throw at me,' she murmured, her eyes hotting up too.

His breathing quickened. 'I know I said I'd drop the casting couch stuff...but do you think you could handle some love-games?'

'What did you have in mind?' she whispered, moving her nude body provocatively against his.

He groaned hoarsely, burying his hot face in her neck. 'Chris, I don't want you to feel I haven't meant a word I've said...it's just that the thought of it still makes me burn up like a fire-cracker and go wild with desire!'

'Me too!' She ran her hands deliberately down to his taut buttocks, feeling the sudden, rigid tension growing again all over his body, locking his spine, tightening every muscle, making his manhood stretch her inside excitingly. 'And I want to play love-games as often as possible when we're married...I'm an actress, remember? I love to act. And I love to excite my audience...'

'Well, you've got me seriously excited!' he drawled thickly, laughing, and raised his head to kiss her. 'I just want you to know it'll always be the icing on the cake. It's you I love. What you are, what you were, what you've made of yourself, and what you will be...'

'I'll be so much more,' she whispered, 'if stay with me forever.'

'Oh, I'll be with you until doomsday!' he said thickly, lowering his head to kiss her. 'Till the skies turn cold, the stars fall to earth and the moon herself turns to blue fire...'

Christie wrapped her arms around his neck as the kiss deepened, and lost herself in his arms, secure in her love now, and able to set her career, ambition and secret fears aside just because she had the love of this man, this one, perfect—because he was as imperfect as her—man.

And as he made love to her, it was she, not the moon, who turned to blue fire...

Cruel Legacy

One man's untimely death deprives a wife of her husband, robs a man of his job and offers someone else the chance of a lifetime...

Suicide — the only way out for Andrew Ryecart, facing crippling debt. An end to his troubles, but for those he leaves behind the problems are just beginning, as the repercussions of this most desperate of acts reach out and touch the lives of six different people — changing them forever.

Special large-format paperback edition

OCTOBER
£8.99

THREE LOVE STORIES...

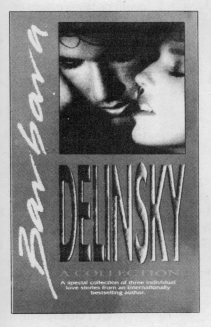

A beautiful collection of three individual love stories from *New York Times* bestselling author Barbara Delinsky – each featuring the charming and irrepressible matchmaker, Victoria Lesser.

A very collectable volume, offering new fans the chance to sample some of Delinsky's earlier works and for long-time fans to collect an edition to treasure.

W◑RLDWIDE

Next Month's Romances

Each month you can choose from a wide variety of romance with Mills & Boon. Below are the new titles to look out for next month, why not ask either Mills & Boon Reader Service or your Newsagent to reserve you a copy of the titles you want to buy – just tick the titles you would like and either post to Reader Service or take it to any Newsagent and ask them to order your books.

Please save me the following titles:	Please tick	✓
DANGEROUS ALLIANCE	*Helen Bianchin*	
INDECENT DECEPTION	*Lynne Graham*	
SAVAGE COURTSHIP	*Susan Napier*	
RELENTLESS FLAME	*Patricia Wilson*	
NOTHING CHANGES LOVE	*Jacqueline Baird*	
READY FOR ROMANCE	*Debbie Macomber*	
DETERMINED LADY	*Margaret Mayo*	
TEQUILA SUNRISE	*Anne Weale*	
A THORN IN PARADISE	*Cathy Williams*	
UNCHAINED DESTINIES	*Sara Wood*	
WORLDS APART	*Kay Thorpe*	
CAPTIVE IN EDEN	*Karen van der Zee*	
OLD DESIRES	*Liz Fielding*	
HEART OF THE JAGUAR	*Rebecca King*	
YESTERDAY'S VOWS	*Vanessa Grant*	
THE ALEXAKIS BRIDE	*Anne McAllister*	

If you would like to order these books in addition to your regular subscription from Mills & Boon Reader Service please send £1.90 per title to: Mills & Boon Reader Service, Freepost, P.O. Box 236, Croydon, Surrey, CR9 9EL, quote your Subscriber No:.................................... (if applicable) and complete the name and address details below. Alternatively, these books are available from many local Newsagents including W H Smith, J Menzies, Martins and other paperback stockists from 11 November 1994.

Name:...

Address:..

....Post Code:..........................

To Retailer: If you would like to stock M&B books please contact your regular book/magazine wholesaler for details.